Planned Beef Production
and Marketing

Planned Beef Production and Marketing

David Allen

BSP PROFESSIONAL BOOKS

OXFORD LONDON EDINBURGH

BOSTON MELBOURNE

First published 1990

British Library
Cataloguing in Publication Data
Allen, David
  Planned beef production and marketing.
  Great Britain. Livestock. Cattle beef.
  Production
  I. Title
  636.2130941

ISBN 0–632–02611–1

BSP Professional Books
A division of Blackwell Scientific
  Publications Ltd
Editorial Offices:
Osney Mead, Oxford OX2 0EL
  (Orders: Tel. 0865 240201)
25 John Street, London WC1N 2BL
23 Ainslie Place, Edinburgh EH3 6AJ
3 Cambridge Center, Suite 208, Cambridge
  MA 02142, USA
107 Barry Street, Carlton, Victoria 3053,
  Australia

Set by DP Photosetting, Aylesbury, Bucks
Printed in Great Britain by
St Edmundsbury Press Ltd
Bury St Edmunds, Suffolk.

Contents

Preface

This book is a sequel to *Planned Beef Production* written by Brian Kilkenny and myself. When the revised edition was published in 1984 we realised that the next step was a new book but doubted whether we could find the time to write it. Then entering private practice as a consultant I realised that I could indeed write a new book using the time spared from office routine and endless committee meetings. Unfortunately, Brian Kilkenny has been unable to join me as co-author as he has now moved into retail marketing.

I have modelled the book on its predecessor with sections on principles, planning and production. Throughout there is a strong emphasis on marketing.

Chapters have been written at different levels deliberately. The chapter on buildings and equipment, for example, is only an introduction to a major subject. Those on growth, breeding, feeding and grassland management are reviews of subjects each of which could be a book in its own right. The descriptions of production systems are comprehensive.

I am grateful to several associates who read chapters for me and offered expert comment – Dr Tony Kempster (growth), David Steane (breeding), Dick Baker (grassland), Archie Sains (marketing) and Julian Bryan and Alan Spedding (planning and production systems). Special thanks are due to Annie Dubery for producing the manuscript.

Part of Table 3.1 and Tables 3.3, 3.5, 3.6 and 3.7 from ADAS leaflet P2087 are used with the permission of the Ministry of Agriculture, Fisheries and Food © Crown Copyright, 1989. Table 3.4 is reproduced with the permission of the International Association of Fishmeal Manufacturers. Figure 7.2 has been constructed from information in NIAB Technical Leaflet No. 2.

My old organisation, the Meat and Livestock Commission (MLC) has kindly allowed me to quote freely from its published work. I hope this demonstrates just how influential MLC has been in beef breeding and production and raises concern at the extent to which resources have been withdrawn from livestock improvement. Farmers' leaders have let this happen, unable or unwilling to recognise the importance of production efficiency and preferring advertising, export promotion and work on meat quality. Important though these subjects are, in the coming years it is farmers who are likely to make the greatest contribution to reducing the real cost of beef, a meat which consumers like but consider expensive. Farmers need the support of MLC in this quest.

Research is in a muddle in Great Britain because of massive government cuts in funding for so-called 'near market' research. Industry organisations are struggling to pick up the pieces but good scientists and good work are being lost. Private funding of research has helped but commercial organisations expect 'intellectual property rights', i.e. to own the answers, and so more research is being done behind closed doors.

It is inconceivable that such a situation would be allowed to develop in major agricultural countries such as France, Holland and the USA, though everywhere there is pressure to become more cost-effective.

Shining through the gloom there is a band of experienced professionals and young talent who, despite the difficulties under which they now work, keep producing new ideas and guidance on how these can be put to work on farms.

Planned production systems have gained widespread acceptance in recent years. Through the mid-1980s sale prices for slaughter cattle were stagnant or declining and farmers had to adopt a more organised approach to production, in particular offsetting declining margins per head by increasing stocking rates on grassland.

EEC milk quotas, first imposed in 1984, have led to a reduction in dairy cow numbers creating room for suckler herd expansion. Nowhere is a planned approach to production more important.

Marketing as well as production needs to be planned. EEC policy is moving away from supporting end prices which makes market forces more obvious and is a stimulus for better marketing.

There is growing consumer concern about the safety and wholesomeness of meat and the welfare of animals producing it. The EEC ban on hormone implants, which has no scientific basis, provides a telling example of how powerful the consumer lobby can be. The moral is that consumer interests must be kept fully informed of new developments so that their expression of wants is based on a proper evaluation of facts rather than heresay.

The twin challenges of the 1990s are the single European market and biotechnology. The single market, due to be in force from the start of 1993, will open up intra-Community trade and give it a more competitive edge. Biotechnological advances in embryo transfer and genetic engineering have the power to transform the structure of the cattle industry giving control over sex and genetic design. Both of these challenges will be turned to greatest advantage by planned production and marketing.

David Allen

1 The Beef Industry

Cattle were first domesticated at least seven thousand years ago and are now found in every continent. Milk is a key product both in developed agriculture and also in village agriculture in developing countries. People of most races and creeds like beef if it is available and they can afford it.

CATTLE INDUSTRY STRUCTURES

Cattle numbers in the more important cattle-producing countries are shown in Table 1.1. Incredibly, world beef production is within 12 million tonnes (80 per cent) of world pigmeat production (Table 1.2). Poultry meat production is expanding fastest on a world scale.

Various types of beef industry structure have developed depending on climate, land type and population density. Particularly important is the relationship between milk and beef production.

In the rangelands of North and South America, Australia and some parts of Africa cattle are ranched using breeds specialised for beef production; the dairy industry is entirely separate and occurs around the main centres of population. By contrast, throughout much of Europe dairying dominates the cattle industry and beef production is largely, sometimes wholly, a by-product of dairying.

In Great Britain a highly integrated cattle industry structure developed after the Second World War with an important exchange of breeding stock between beef and dairy herds (Figure 1.1). The dairy herd is dominated by Friesian/Holstein cows about half of which are crossed with beef bulls. Male purebred Friesian/Holstein and beef breed × Friesian calves are reared for beef together with some crossbred heifers. However, a proportion of the crossbred heifers are reared as suckler herd replacements and augment traditional cow types such as the Blue Grey bred from mountain breeds. This allows a larger crossbred suckler herd to be maintained than if only the traditional source of replacements were available.

The merits of an integrated structure are so obvious that it is surprising it has not been more widely copied. Dairy cows not needed to breed purebred

Table 1.1 Cattle numbers in selected countries.
(Source: *MLC European Handbook*.)

		1981	1983	1985	1987
		(millions)			
North America	Canada	12.2	12.6	12.2	11.7
	USA	114.3	115.0	109.7	102.0
Central America	Mexico	35.7	37.5	31.5	31.2
South America	Argentina	54.2	53.9	54.0	55.7
	Brazil	93.5	124.9	128.4	131.5
	Colombia	24.3	24.0	23.3	24.0
	Uruguay	11.4	9.7	9.6	10.3
	Venezuela	11.1	11.6	12.1	12.7
Africa	Ethiopia	26.1	26.3	28.0	30.0
	Nigeria	12.5	12.3	11.9	12.2
	South Africa	13.2	13.1	12.0	11.8
	Sudan	18.7	20.5	20.9	20.5
	Tanzania	12.8	13.5	14.0	14.5
Middle East	Turkey	18.0	17.9	12.4	12.4
Far East	Bangladesh	36.6	37.7	23.0	23.5
	China	71.2	75.4	62.7	71.3
	India	244.5	246.4	198.0	199.3
	Pakistan	27.7	28.6	16.5	17.0
Oceania	Australia	25.2	22.5	22.8	23.3
	New Zealand	8.0	7.6	7.9	8.3
Eastern Europe	Poland	11.8	11.3	11.1	10.5
	USSR	115.1	117.5	121.1	122.1
EEC	Belgium	2.9	3.1	3.1	3.1
	Denmark	2.9	2.9	2.6	2.3
	West Germany	15.0	15.7	16.0	15.4
	Greece	0.8	0.8	0.8	0.8
	France	22.5	24.3	23.7	22.3
	Ireland	5.6	6.9	6.9	6.6
	Italy	8.9	9.1	9.2	8.9
	Luxembourg	0.2	0.2	0.2	0.2
	Netherlands	5.0	5.3	5.2	4.9
	UK	13.1	13.3	12.9	12.2
	Spain	na	na	5.0	5.0
	Portugal	na	na	na	1.3

na: not available

Table 1.2 World meat production.
(Source: FAO.)

	1981	1983	1985	1987
	(million tonnes)			
Beef and buffalo	43.9	45.8	47.8	49.7
Sheep and goat	7.8	7.9	8.4	8.7
Pig	51.9	53.9	59.3	61.6
Poultry	27.1	29.1	32.0	35.2

replacements are crossed to beef bulls thereby producing calves of improved beef merit. Crossbred females from these matings are used as suckler cows showing good hybrid vigour.

Only Ireland has a similar structure. In France there is a good deal of beef crossing in dairy herds but no use is made of the crossbred females as suckler cows; virtually all suckler cows are purebreds. Elsewhere in Western Europe even beef crossing in dairy herds is at an early stage of development.

The imposition of EEC milk quotas in 1984, with a further constriction in 1987, is changing cattle industry structures in Western Europe. For example, beef herds are being introduced into West Germany which previously had few beef cows. Some EEC countries, notably France and the UK, have always had both beef and dairy herds with the beef herds kept on poorer land not suited to dairying.

Numbers of beef and dairy cows in EEC countries shown in Table 1.3 demonstrate the dominance of the dairy herd. However, since the advent of milk quotas the proportion of beef cows has increased from 18 per cent of total cows in 1984 to 23 per cent in 1988 and is set to increase further.

EEC dairy farmers, restricted in the amount of milk they can produce, have looked at other ways of maintaining their income. In Britain, for example, the level of beef crossing in dairy herds is now about 50 per cent having been stable at 35–40 per cent for many years prior to 1984.

Also, beef breed usage for crossing with dairy cows has changed with a swing away from the Hereford to the continental beef breeds (Table 1.4). The AI statistics in the table refer mainly to cow matings and there is still considerable use of easy calving breeds such as Angus and Hereford for natural service heifers, though even here greater use is being made of the Limousin with its intermediate level of calving difficulty. Farmers are prepared to learn how to cope with potentially more difficult calvings for the sake of the higher value of the continental breed × Friesian calf.

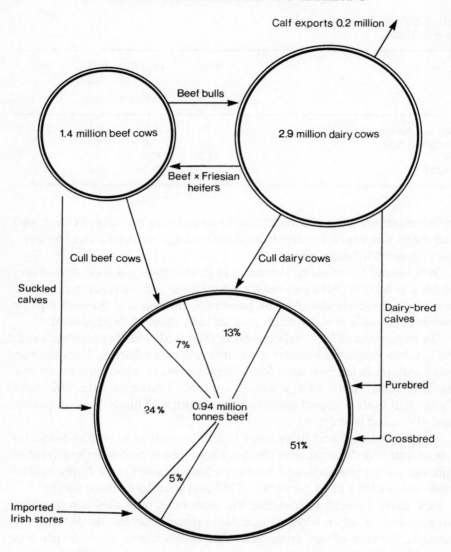

Fig. 1.1 Cattle industry structure in the UK, 1988. (Source: *MLC UK Handbook*.)

The increase in beef crossing in dairy herds and the swing to thickly muscled continental breeds is doing much to ameliorate the penetration of the Friesian breed by specialist dairy Holsteins from North America which are inferior for beef production to the dual purpose Friesian and all beef breed crosses out of Friesians. In addition, as dairy cow numbers continue to decline and beef cow numbers increase, the proportion of beef produced

Table 1.3 Numbers of beef and dairy cows in EEC countries. (Source: Statistical Office of the European Community.)

	1982		1984		1986		1988*	
	Dairy	Beef	Dairy	Beef	Dairy	Beef	Dairy	Beef
			(millions)					
Belgium	0.97	0.14	0.99	0.16	0.95	0.20	0.89	0.24
Denmark	1.00	0.06	0.95	0.06	0.86	0.06	0.77	0.07
France	7.01	3.00	6.93	3.06	6.30	3.34	5.42	3.26
Greece	0.24	0.15	0.22	0.15	0.24	0.13	0.24	0.14
Ireland	1.59	0.43	1.64	0.44	1.58	0.44	1.48	0.48
Italy	3.05	0.77	3.27	0.42	3.07	0.42	3.06	0.42
Luxembourg	0.07	0.01	0.07	0.02	0.07	0.02	0.06	0.02
Netherlands	2.49	—	2.58	—	2.33	—	2.04	—
Portugal	na		na				0.42	0.20
Spain	na		1.90	0.77	1.86	0.79	1.83	0.97
United Kingdom	3.25	1.39	3.28	1.35	3.14	1.31	2.91	1.37
West Germany	5.41	0.13	5.68	0.15	5.42	0.17	4.99	0.18
EEC total	25.07	6.04	25.62	5.80	23.97	6.07	24.11	7.34

na: not available
* EEC 12

Table 1.4 Trends in beef crossing in dairy herds.
(Source: Milk Marketing Board.)

Breed	1971	1984–85	1985–86	1986–87	1987–88	1988–89
			(000 inseminations)			
Angus	134	43	45	61	62	68
Belgian Blue	—	6	17	79	116	112
Blonde d'Aquitaine	—	8	9	19	29	31
Charolais	121	137	118	205	217	222
Hereford	546	279	192	226	161	143
Limousin	—	169	204	404	337	281
Simmental	5	25	27	74	86	98
Total beef AI	841	686	629	1096	1035	984

from dairy bred cattle is set to fall, having increased sharply between 1978 and 1985 (Table 1.5). This trend is likely to be reinforced by EEC policy which, scared of surpluses, favours extensive production methods.

Source is only one aspect of type of production. The other is the categories of beef which are produced – cow, bull, steer, heifer, veal. To some extent categories are dependent on the cattle industry structure but they also

Table 1.5 Sources of beef production in the UK.
(Source: MLC Beef Yearbooks, Author's forecasts.)

	UK beef production (million tonnes)	Cull cows Dairy	Beef	Clean cattle Dairy	Beef	Irish stores
			(% of production)			
1978	1.02	19	6	39	28	8
1979	1.04	19	6	41	28	6
1980	1.10	20	6	41	28	5
1981	1.04	16	5	46	29	4
1982	0.95	17	5	46	28	4
1983	1.04	14	6	48	27	5
1984	1.15	16	5	49	24	5
1985	1.15	13	6	53	24	4
1986	1.06	14	5	52	23	6
1987	1.10	16	5	52	23	4
1988	0.94	13	7	51	24	5
1989f	0.95	15	5	49	27	4
1990f	0.96	15	5	48	28	4

f: forecast

Table 1.6 Categories of beef production in selected EEC countries, 1986.
(Source: Statistical Office of the European Community.)

	Cows	Bulls	Steers	Heifers	Veal	Total production (000 tonnes)
Belgium	33	31	4	19	13	317
Denmark	44	45	1	9	1	244
Greece	11	68	0	14	7	82
France	35	18	14	14	19	1910
Ireland	18	1	61	20	<1	511
Italy	15	61	1	7	16	1176
Luxembourg	40	30	10	20	0	10
Netherlands	39	20	0	6	35	540
UK	19	6	49	26	<1	1046
West Germany	27	53	1	14	5	1695

(% of home production)

depend on live cattle imports/exports, consumer preference and the evolution of production systems. The situation in selected EEC countries is presented in Table 1.6.

In general, countries with a high proportion of cow beef have high levels of calf exports (e.g. France, West Germany), a large veal industry (e.g. Netherlands), or both. France and Germany add to home-produced cow beef by importing supplies from other EEC countries.

The large majority of male cattle are reared as bulls except in the UK, Ireland and to a lesser extent France. In the UK bull beef production is expanding steadily.

The proportion of heifer beef depends on the ratio of dairy to beef cows, the size of the veal industry and the number of bull calves imported. It is highest in the UK where there is a relatively large suckler herd and a minute veal industry.

The most important veal-producing countries in the EEC are France, Italy and the Netherlands. The prospect is that veal production will decline because the high cost of calves and milk replacer make production unprofitable. In addition, public concern about the welfare of veal calves probably spells an end to 'white veal' as it is now recognised.

THE EEC BEEF REGIME

The EEC beef regime exercises influential control over beef production, trade flows within the EEC and trade with non-EEC countries. The main plank of EEC support for beef production has been 'intervention'. In principle this is a regulatory mechanism designed to support market prices by purchasing specified qualities and categories of beef and removing it from the market when prices are low and selling it back into the market when prices are high.

In practice the intervention system has been an expensive failure. It has proved unable to support market prices and as a result became a permanent feature of the market instead of a safety net. The result of this was the build-up of a huge beef mountain with almost 0.7 million tonnes in store in 1987. This mountain has only recently started to be flattened at high cost. Almost certainly it would have been cheaper to eat the 'surplus' at a low price as it was produced, allowing price as well as support measures to adjust future levels of production.

Radical changes were made to the intervention system in 1989 designed to limit its use and cost. Now the maximum amount purchased in a marketing year is restricted to 220,000 tonnes. Access to intervention still depends on market prices falling below a predetermined minimum but the price paid for the beef going into intervention is determined by competitive tender. In the event of market prices collapsing safety net procedures would come into force.

Associated with intervention is a private storage aids scheme under which meat traders remove beef from the market and are paid to store it for a specified period before selling it. The beef never passes into intervention.

Exports to third countries are encouraged by export refunds which vary according to the quality of beef being traded with different rates of payment for various world zones. These export refunds are highly controversial with countries competing with EEC in world markets. They see a high price market being propped up by subsidies in the EEC, to which they are largely denied access by high customs duties, but exports being heavily subsidised in the world market and depressing their prices. The controversy is not surprising given the high volume of world trade (Table 1.7).

EEC prices for agricultural products are set at a common level in European Currency Units (ECUs) and are converted to national currencies using so-called green exchange rates. The system is designed to allow trading among member states despite differences in actual exchange rates. However, because of political manipulation of the green currency system, Monetary Compensatory Amounts (MCAs) had to be introduced to allow for variations in exchange rates. MCAs are reviewed weekly and if a negative MCA applies, indicating a weak or depreciating currency, it operates as a refund on imports and a levy on exports.

General support for beef producers in the EEC is provided through the

Table 1.7 World trade in beef and veal.
(Source: *MLC European Handbook*.)

		1983	1984	1985	1986	1987
		(000 tonnes)				
EEC	Imports	448	414	489	465	496
	Exports	603	790	805	1167	909
USA	Imports	566	516	595	630	671
	Exports	81	99	100	168	200
Canada	Imports	58	78	76	76	92
Japan	Imports	137	146	151	179	220
Argentina	Exports	415	250	260	256	287
Australia	Exports	504	386	437	515	584
Brazil	Exports	120	115	140	80	60
New Zealand	Exports	228	196	221	209	275
Uruguay	Exports	161	97	92	127	52

special beef premium, the suckler cow premium and hill livestock compensatory allowances.

The special beef premium was introduced to the UK in 1989 and replaced the beef variable premium which had operated since 1976. This brought the UK in line with other member states. Producers receive a single headage payment on a maximum of 90 male cattle (bulls or steers) each year. There is no quality standard but cattle must weigh at least 370 kg liveweight (or 200 kg deadweight).

The former beef variable premium had the attraction that it paid the difference between the average market price and a seasonal target price up to a maximum value per kg. Cattle only qualified for payment if they were above a minimum conformation standard and not overfat. In the end the conformation standard became a burden to the scheme because it impeded the market's valuation of quality differentials.

The suckler cow premium was introduced in 1980 and the basic EEC premium can be supplemented up to a maximum value from national funds, as it is in the UK. It is generally assumed that the EEC will favour this type of subsidy in future, in preference to market price support, in the promotion of more extensive systems of management.

The hill livestock compensatory allowance (HLCA) scheme was introduced in 1976 to recognise the difficulties of farming in 'less favoured areas'. The EEC funds 25 per cent of the cost. In 1985 the original less favoured areas were extended at a lower rate of allowance. Now the scheme covers all marginal and sub-marginal land.

For further reading on this bureaucratic jungle the reader is referred to the admirable *MLC UK Handbook* or *MLC European Handbook*.

1992

By the end of 1992 the EEC is dedicated to dismantling physical, technical and fiscal barriers to trade so that a single European market is created. It is sometimes called the internal market.

Physical barriers refer to border controls on goods, livestock and citizens and include customs and health checks. Technical barriers include such things as food laws and additive regulations. The removal of fiscal barriers is largely to do with the harmonisation of rates of VAT and excise duty.

The single market proposals will have major effects on the beef sector. Particularly important is creating common animal health and meat hygiene regulations but food regulations are also important.

Common EEC standards will be set for animal health status and meat hygiene within which cattle and meat can be traded freely whilst still preventing the spread of disease. Disease eradication programmes, allied to the identification of disease-free zones and herds will become the basis of trading. Alongside these arrangements a standard method will be adopted for inspecting imports from outside the EEC.

There is some doubt whether the timetable for the single market can be met but provided the main provisions are in place by the end of 1992, the new arrangements should be a considerable stimulus to intra-community trade. For example, it would be a fillip to the UK trade in 'traditional beef' into continental catering outlets. At the same time trading will become more competitive.

It is important to realise that, even when the single market is established, the provisions of the EEC support regime will still have an overriding influence on the beef sector.

EVOLUTION OF THE BEEF INDUSTRY

The pressures for evolution of the beef industry vary in different parts of the world. In Western Europe, North America, Australia and New Zealand the talk is of surpluses. But over much of the globe underproduction is the problem. In many of the communist countries of Eastern Europe political dogma has failed to deliver beef into butchers' shops. All too widely in Africa, armed insurrection and hunger go hand in hand. And the decline of the once great South American beef industry is sad.

Everywhere environmental conservation will be the theme of the 1990s. How it will best be served by the cattle industry needs to be thought through with some care. It may well be that in Western Europe more extensive production is a sound route. However, in other situations greater productivity will serve the cause better because it brings a reduction in cattle numbers, taking pressure off fragile environments (and reducing methane production which also contributes to destruction of the ozone layer).

Meanwhile technological development gathers pace. Biotechnological advances in embryo transfer and genetic engineering have the power to transform cattle industry structures over the next decade.

Cows could be surrogates for single or twin embryos purpose-bred for milk, beef or maternal qualities. It is not yet clear how much of this new technology will be acceptable to the public. Nor is it entirely clear how much of it can be applied, especially in developing countries, or even if it is needed.

Some of these issues are explored in the ensuing chapters together with the more ordinary, but vitally important, business of using existing knowledge to produce high quality beef at lower cost.

2 Growth, Carcase Development and Meat Quality

The beef producer is a manager of growth and development which yields the lean, fat and bone from which retail cuts of meat are prepared. The carcase objective is a high proportion of lean, minimum bone and only the amount of fat demanded by the market.

To the extent that the producer can influence the proportions of carcase tissues, an understanding of growth and development is very important. Moreover, since meat from some parts of the carcase is more valuable than from other parts, it is important to know what factors influence the distribution of tissues within the carcase and whether it is possible to manipulate body proportions.

GROWTH

When cattle are fed a high quality diet *ad libitum* growth is linear over a long period until it starts falling away as mature size is approached. Rate of growth and the point at which it declines are affected by breed and sex. Heavy, lean continental breeds such as the Charolais grow faster than smaller breeds such as the Angus and growth rate tapers off later. Sex also has its effects, bulls growing faster than steers which in turn grow faster than heifers.

Level of feeding has crucial effects on growth rate. Usually growth is non-linear because of seasonal variations in the supply and quality of feeds. An important homeostatic mechanism called compensatory growth causes cattle which have been underfed during the winter or through a dry season to grow especially fast when full feeding resumes and to catch up on cattle which have been full-fed throughout. Compensatory growth is an evolutionary device which allows cattle to cope with seasonal feed shortages yet still reach mature size. It can also be exploited in commercial cattle management to save expensive winter feeds for cattle which are to be grazed on high quality pasture.

In fact the nature of growth is such that even when growth has been retarded by pre-partum influences such as twin pregnancy, first pregnancy, underfeeding or premature birth, cattle usually attain their normal mature size eventually, albeit at an older age than when growth has not been retarded. Only when restriction is very severe indeed is permanent stunting a possibility.

Killing-out percentage

Liveweight gain measures not only the accumulation of carcase tissues but also the increasing weight of the hide, head, feet, internal organs, body fluids and contents of the gut. The proportion of the liveweight yielded as carcase weight is called the *killing-out* or *dressing percentage* which ranges typically between 50 and 60 per cent.

Several factors affect the killing-out percentage. It is about 2 per cent higher when the carcase is weighed hot than when it is weighed cold. If the dressing specification includes removal of the kidney knob and channel fat (KKCF), which is the British convention, the killing-out percentage is about 2 per cent lower than when this fat depot is left in place. Variations in gut fill have specially important effects on killing-out percentage. Gut fill declines during fasting, for example when cattle are being transported to market.

In general as cattle grow heavier and become fatter the killing-out percentage increases. Also there are important differences between breeds and the muscular continental European breeds kill out better than the native British breeds. Double-muscled breeds such as the Belgian Blue and Pie-montese have particularly high killing-out percentages.

Given the large number of factors influencing killing-out percentage and its variability it is not surprising that buyers in live auction markets take a pride in their claim to be able to judge it. Killing-out percentage is very important when cattle are purchased live because it determines the net cost per kg of carcase.

CARCASE DEVELOPMENT

The development of the carcase is governed by three overlapping processes:

(a) Bone achieves its maximum growth rate first, followed by muscle and finally fat.
(b) Partition of nutrients gives preference to bone and muscle development over fat. When cattle are fed sub-maintenance diets fat is drawn on preferentially as a source of energy.

(c) A differential growth pattern starts at the extremities of the foetal calf
     and ultimately converges on the abdomen. So at birth the calf is bony,
     with a big head and feet connected by long legs to a slight body.

At birth muscle is the heaviest carcase tissue and it continues to gain faster
than the other tissues during juvenile growth with a resulting increase in the
muscle:bone ratio. As the animal approaches maturity a fattening phase
takes over and in grossly overfat mature cattle the weight of fat can equal the
weight of muscle.

The fat depots in the carcase are filled in the order KKCF, intermuscular
(seam) fat, subcutaneous fat and intramuscular (marbling) fat. KKCF, seam
fat and subcutaneous fat above market requirements are detrimental to
carcase quality. As will be seen later, marbling fat has beneficial effects on
the eating quality of beef.

Work by the late Sir John Hammond and his group at the University of
Cambridge either side of the Second World War concluded that the regional
development of the carcase allowed slaughter to be timed when muscles of
the most valuable cuts were at their best relative development, and so
comprised the highest possible percentage of the carcase. In particular, the
valuable loin joint was characterised as late maturing. Subsequent dissection
studies, however, do not bear out this proposition.

Certainly there is an ordered development of the muscles. It is essential,
for example, that at birth muscles enabling the calf to stand, suckle and
move on with the herd must be relatively well developed. Thereafter,
muscles at the ends of the limbs develop relatively less than those in the
upper limbs or surrounding the spinal column. It is the muscles of the
abdominal wall which are latest maturing. The important point is that these
developmental changes are largely complete long before slaughter age.

This does not deny that as development proceeds the conformation of
cattle alters. Changes in skeletal dimensions are small relative to the increase
in muscle weight and thickness. Also, muscles are pushed apart as
intermuscular fat develops between them and the whole musculature is
covered by a layer of subcutaneous fat which increases in thickness as
fattening proceeds.

Most cattlemen and meat traders prefer carcases of good conformation
because 'they have more meat in the right places'. If this is so it is important
because there are considerable differences in retail prices between high and
low value cuts (Figure 2.1).

It is equally obvious to meat scientists who have dissected large numbers
of carcases that, although the percentage of lean varies, this lean is
distributed between cuts in a singularly constant manner. The MLC breed

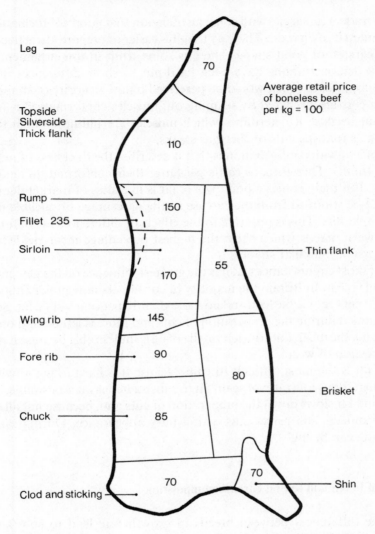

Fig. 2.1 Relative values of carcase cuts based on retail values. (Source: J.B. Kilkenny (personal communication).)

evaluation results in Table 4.1 show that in scraggy Holstein carcases 43.8 per cent of the lean was in the high-priced cuts, yet admirable Limousin × Friesian carcases had a value only 1.9 percentage units higher. (An exception is the double-muscled Culard in which the muscles of the upper limbs are developed more than the fibrous muscles at the extremities.)

More important than the distribution of lean is the fact that, at the same fatness, carcases of better conformation have a higher percentage of lean.

Meat traders can argue with some justification that good conformation is important in its own right. They say that it is easier to prepare attractive cuts from a carcase of good shape. There is some truth in this argument but butchery demonstrations have been hard-put to show differences in the appearance of cuts which would be perceived by the majority of shoppers.

When cuts are prepared by seaming out muscles conformation is more important because it determines which muscles are plump enough to be prepared as roasting cuts or sliced as steaks.

A problem with conformation is that it describes the thickness of muscle plus fat (flesh). Therefore, as cattle get fatter their conformation tends to improve. But there comes a point where fat is in excess of market demand and must be trimmed from the carcase so the percentage of saleable meat begins to decline. This is opposite to the effects of differences in conformation between breeds which show the highest percentage meat yields from lean breeds of muscular shape.

Under most circumstances fat has the greatest influence on the percentage of saleable meat. In Britain the majority of consumers now prefer cuts with at least 90 per cent visible lean and no more than 10 per cent visible fat. Some fat is trimmed during the preparation of cuts and more is left behind on the plate during the meal. Fat trim left on the plate is undesirable because it gives the impression of waste.

Seam fat is the most difficult to trim because it is hard to get at with a knife. Therefore a low ratio of seam fat to subcutaneous fat is desirable. Too much seam fat slows down the preparation of cuts and, because not all of it can be removed, still leaves cuts with a fatty appearance. During eating, plate waste can be high.

Effects of breed and sex on carcase composition

The large differences between breeds in growth rate lead to substantial differences in the absolute weights of carcase tissues at a stated age. Moreover, these effects are added to by breed differences in the age at which the fattening phase gets under way. Typically the native British breeds such as Angus and Hereford have a relatively early fattening phase and can be described as early maturing. By contrast, the continental European breeds such as Charolais and Simmental are lean with a later fattening phase; they are described as late maturing.

Most of the fast-growing breeds are late maturing but growth rate and rate of maturity do not always go hand in hand. For example, among the early maturing British breeds there is considerable variation in growth rate.

Table 2.1 Carcase characteristics of crossbred cattle from dairy herds reared in an 18-month beef system.
(Source: Adapted from Kempster, A.J., Cook, G.L. and Southgate, J.R.. (1988) *Animal Production*, **46**, 365–378.)

Breed type	Killing-out %	Carcase weight (kg)	Conformation (15-point scale)	Lean (%)	Lean:bone ratio	Lean in high-priced cuts (%)
Friesian (F)	51.3	240	4.6	61.5	3.6	44.8
Holstein	50.5	265	2.5	59.6	3.4	43.8
Charolais × F	53.2	277	8.1	63.6	4.0	45.3
Hereford × F	50.9	203	5.9	62.3	3.8	45.1
Limousin × F	53.7	247	7.1	64.2	4.2	45.7
Lincoln Red × F	50.4	213	5.1	61.9	3.8	45.4
Simmental × F	52.2	257	6.2	62.5	3.9	45.6
South Devon × F	52.3	231	5.9	62.4	3.9	45.0
Sussex × F	51.1	210	6.4	63.0	3.9	44.8

Table 2.2 Carcase characteristics of crossbred cattle from suckler herds.
(Source: Adapted from Kempster, A.J., Cook, G.L. and Southgate, J.R.. (1988) *Animal Production*, **35**, 99–111.)

Sire breed*	Killing-out (%)	Carcase weight (kg)	Conformation (15-point scale)	Saleable meat %	Saleable meat:bone ratio	Saleable meat in high-priced cuts (%)
Winter finishing						
Angus	52.5	205	9.9	72.5	4.1	44.1
Charolais	54.8	268	11.2	72.7	4.0	44.8
Devon	52.7	219	8.6	71.6	3.9	44.0
Hereford	52.3	214	8.7	71.9	3.9	44.1
Limousin	54.7	247	11.0	73.3	4.2	45.4
Lincoln Red	52.3	222	8.5	70.8	3.8	44.3
Murray Grey	53.4	215	9.1	72.0	4.1	44.3
Simmental	53.0	258	9.9	72.0	3.9	44.8
South Devon	53.2	237	8.1	72.0	3.9	44.3
Sussex	53.1	226	9.5	72.6	4.0	43.9
Summer finishing						
Angus	51.0	206	10.1	72.0	4.0	44.0
Charolais	52.7	275	11.0	71.9	3.9	44.8
Devon	51.0	224	9.3	71.3	3.9	43.9
Hereford	51.1	224	9.9	71.4	3.8	44.4
Lincoln Red	50.9	235	8.8	70.7	3.8	44.1
Simmental	52.2	272	10.9	71.7	3.9	44.7
South Devon	51.8	251	8.7	71.2	3.8	44.1
Sussex	51.8	237	9.9	71.6	4.0	44.1

* Half calves out of Hereford × Friesian cows and half out of Blue Grey (Shorthorn × Galloway).

Also, among the late maturing breeds there are some, of which the Limousin is the best example, which are of medium growth rate.

Differences in proportions of carcase tissues are due largely to the age of onset of fattening. However, there are also important differences in muscle:bone ratio. Generally, thickly muscled breeds such as Limousin and breeds with a light bone structure such as Angus and Sussex have the highest muscle:bone ratios.

These and other effects of breed on carcase composition are demonstrated by results from MLC breed comparisons in which the cattle were all slaughtered at the same subcutaneous fat cover on the carcase (Tables 2.1 and 2.2). The dairy beef results have carcase composition presented as the percentage lean but the suckler beef results as the percentage saleable beef. As a rough guide saleable meat with a typical supermarket fat cover is 1.15 × percentage lean. Companion cattle performance results are presented in Chapter 4, Tables 4.5 and 4.6.

The results showed substantial differences in carcase weight at the same fat cover caused by differences in growth rate and earliness of maturing. Differences in the percentage of lean or saleable meat were quite small. However, the lean breeds of muscular shape had, not only the highest values for percentage lean/saleable meat, but also a slightly higher proportion of it in the high-priced grilling and roasting cuts.

The breeds of dairy origin produced the poorest carcases. Worst of all was the Canadian Holstein which killed out lower that the British Friesian of the 1970s and produced a carcase of poorer shape with a lower percentage of lean and less of it in the high-priced cuts.

In the last few years use has been made for crossbreeding of double-muscled breeds, notably the Belgian Blue and Piemontese which have extreme muscular shape. They have even higher values for killing-out percentage and saleable meat yield than the best of the single-muscled breeds.

Differences in carcase composition between the sexes are similar to differences between breeds. The bull grows faster and is leaner than the heifer. Slaughtered at the same age as equivalent steers, bulls produce carcases at least 10 per cent heavier yet which are still leaner. It is worth noting that although heifers are, on average, fatter than steers or bulls, at the same fat class the heifer carcase yields a higher percentage of saleable meat because of its higher lean:bone ratio.

Level of feeding and marketing decisions interact with the effects of breed and sex on earliness of maturity to determine the precise composition of the carcase at a given age or weight. The general relationships involved are proposed in Figure 2.2.

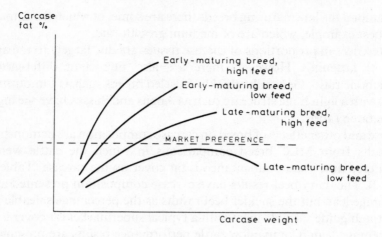

Fig. 2.2 General relationships between carcase weight and carcase fat.

On high quality feeds, early maturing breeds (especially heifers of these breeds) soon reach a stage of development where a substantial proportion of energy storage is as fat. In consequence they must be slaughtered at a relatively early age and light weight to avoid becoming overfat for market demand. By contrast a bull of a late maturing breed stays lean to a high slaughter weight.

Early maturity is not necessarily a disadvantage because adjustments to feeding can be made to control the rate of fattening. On lower quality feeds energy intake is restricted to a point where the opportunity for rapid fattening is denied and the cattle can be carried to a higher commercial slaughter weight. Provided the lower quality feed can be produced cheaply this strategy can be profitable. Feeds of this quality may not only disallow fattening in late maturing types but also restrict muscle growth so that cattle develop the plain appearance of animals emerging from a store period. These interactions between feeding level and earliness of maturity are discussed more fully in Chapter 4.

Manipulation of growth and development

A number of substances the same as or similar to those produced in the body can be used to manipulate growth and development. They include steroid hormones, bovine somatotrophin (BST) and β-adrenergic agonists.

Best known are the steroid hormones which are usually implanted as pellets under the skin of the ear. Responses are very consistent with an

Table 2.3 Responses to hormone implants in 18-month beef steers.
(Source: *MLC Beef Yearbook*, 1986.)

	Non-implanted	Implanted*
Daily gain (kg)	0.87	0.97
Feeding period (days)	369	348
Slaughter weight (kg)	520	529
Carcase weight (kg)	270	277
Carcase shape (1–15 excellent)	4.9	5.4
Composition of thin flank:		
lean (%)	59.3	60.6
sub-cutaneous fat (%)	11.1	12.5
seam fat (%)	19.2	17.0

* Average of oestradiol and zeranol alone and in combination with trenbolone.

increase in daily gain, improved feed conversion efficiency and leaner carcases. In general, oestrogenic substances give the best responses in male cattle and androgenic substances in females. Combinations of oestrogenic and androgenic implants produce an additive response in male cattle.

Table 2.3 shows typical responses for steers in the 18-month beef system. Implanted cattle grew faster and were heavier at slaughter. Dissection of the thin flank from a sample of carcases showed a higher percentage of lean in implanted cattle with an improvement in the ratio of subcutaneous fat to undesirable seam fat.

In bulls the growth response to oestrogen implants is lower than in steers but there is a useful improvement in carcase shape and a slight increase in the percentage of subcutaneous fat (Table 2.4).

It is important to note that in these trials residues of zeranol in the tissues

Table 2.4 Responses to oestrogen implants in cereal beef bulls.
(Source: *MLC Beef Yearbook*, 1986.)

	Trial 1		Trial 2	
	Non-implanted	Oestradiol	Non-implanted	Zeranol
Daily gain (kg)	1.37	1.40	1.38	1.43
Feeding period (days)	222	222	222	215
Slaughter weight (kg)	446	448	449	453
Carcase weight (kg)	237	242	241	245
Carcase shape (1–15 excellent)	6.9	7.7	7.2	8.0
Composition of thin flank:				
lean (%)	66.1	64.8	—	—
sub-cutaneous fat (%)	9.7	10.9	—	—
seam fat (%)	13.0	13.0	—	—

Table 2.5 Responses to androgen implants in heifers and cull cows. (Source: *MLC Beef Yearbook*, 1984 and 1986.)

| | Heifers | | Cull cows | |
	Non-implanted	Implanted	Non-implanted	Implanted
Daily gain (kg)	0.72	0.83	0.92	1.31
Feeding period (days)	120	109	100	100
Slaughter weight (kg)	412	416	553	571
Carcase weight (kg)	215	218	284	301
Carcase shape (1–15 excellent)	6.8	7.3	—	—
Carcase fat (1–15 fat)	9.4	9.2	—	—
Dissection results:				
lean (%)	—	—	62.5	63.3
fat (%)	—	—	19.8	20.0
bone (%)	—	—	15.5	14.6
waste (%)	—	—	2.1	2.1

of steers were only 0.04 parts per billion and in bulls 0.08. These are far lower than residues of the hormones produced naturally in the body.

Both in heifers and cull cows implantation with androgenic hormones produces faster, leaner growth and improved carcase shape (Table 2.5).

In the EEC all hormone implants are now subject to a highly controversial ban. A ban on synthetic stilbene hormones introduced in 1981 was not contested. However, a later ban in 1986 included not only the synthetic substances trenbolone (androgenic) and zeranol (oestrogenic) but also the naturally occurring hormones oestradiol-17β, testosterone and progesterone.

This ban was introduced without awaiting scientific evidence commissioned by the EEC itself. Indeed, the EEC declined to publish the report of its scientific experts led by Professor G.E. Lamming of Nottingham University. To their credit the scientists published their report independently, declaring that all of the substances were safe at recommended dose rates.

To be fair to the consumer activists who campaigned for the ban, there had been a number of incidents of dangerous misuse of hormones. But these all related to black market use of substances in countries where they were banned. And as so many observers warned, with a blanket ban on all hormone implants, black market use is a continuing problem of greater concern than would have been the controlled use of safe licensed products.

The background to the ban on hormone implants has been considered in some detail because it has created a precedent for future legislation. For example, the possible use of BST to increase milk production is already the subject of considerable controversy and all similar products can expect the same rough ride.

The danger is that pharmaceutical companies will decline to risk the high cost of developing new products if legislation is subject to whimsical issues. There are important lessons, too. Consumers now have a powerful voice in food legislation and expect much more information about products than they have had access to in the past. Also, there is growing concern about the safety and wholesomeness of food.

Neither BST nor β-agonists are yet licensed for use in the UK.

BST is analogous with growth hormone and stimulates leaner, more efficient growth in cattle. Growth responses, however, are variable averaging about 12 per cent, i.e. below the response to most hormone implants.

Beta-agonists are substances similar to adrenalin and have remarkable effects on lean percentage and muscularity. Growth responses are variable and rather small on average but feed efficiency is improved by up to 30 per cent despite reduced feed intake. This is associated with a 5–10 per cent increase in lean at the expense of fat. There is some evidence that the effects on carcase composition are reversed quite quickly after withdrawal of the drug which would have practical consequences if the drug was eventually licensed with a withdrawal period.

There are still important questions to be answered about the effects of β-agonists on meat quality. Already it has been demonstrated that carcases from treated cattle are more prone to dark cutting. Also it is possible that the effects on lean percentage are so extreme that drip loss is increased and the meat tougher to eat. If confirmed these effects may disqualify β-agonists for use in cattle solely on the grounds of impaired meat quality.

It has been suggested that immunological approaches to the regulation of growth and development may be preferred to the use of pharmacological products by consumers who are discomfited by the thought of food being 'tampered with'. For example, it may be possible to immunise cattle against the somatostatin which inhibits growth hormone release. Or immunisation against the proteins in the membranes of fat cells might be used to reduce fat content. There was considerable publicity for these approaches in the lead-up to the ban on hormone implants but little progress, however, has been reported since.

CARCASE CLASSIFICATION

The terms carcase classification and carcase grading are inclined to get confused in people's minds. Classification is the description of carcase type. Grading attaches financial values to carcase descriptions. Given the different preferences of meat buyers and trends over time, it is sensible to use carcase classification to describe carcase quality.

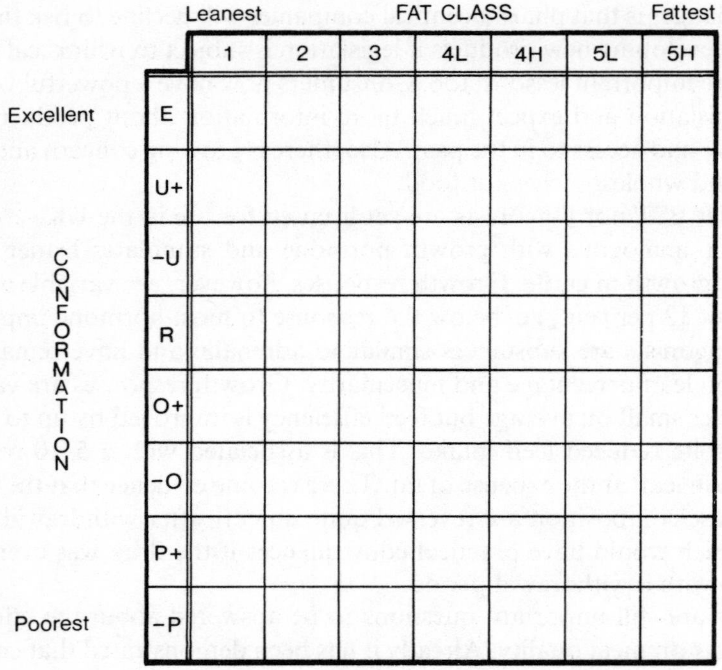

		Leanest			FAT CLASS			Fattest
		1	2	3	4L	4H	5L	5H
Excellent	E							
	U+							
	−U							
	R							
	O+							
	−O							
	P+							
Poorest	−P							

(left axis label: CONFORMATION)

Fig. 2.3 EEC carcase classification grid.

The EEC (EUROP) carcase classification scheme, operated in Great Britain by MLC, classifies conformation and fatness in a grid. Carcase weight and sex are also recorded with an optional estimate of age by reference to dentition.

The evaluation of conformation and fatness is by visual assessments checked against photographic scales. Conformation classes are described by letters from the word Europe, with E for excellent, U, R, O and P for poor. Conformation classes U, O and P are subdivided into better (+) and poorer (−) classes. Fatness is scored from 1 (leanest) to 5 (fattest) with 4 and 5 subdivided into fatter H and leaner L classes. The grid is illustrated in Figure 2.3.

The uptake of carcase classification in Britain at 33 per cent of clean cattle slaughterings in 1987 was disappointing. One of the main reasons for this is political bickering about the cost of the service and who should pay. Since April 1989 carcase classification has been offered as a commercial service, uncluttered by any association with EEC price support measures, and will probably achieve a much higher level of use provided the price of the service is right.

% of carcases

				Fatness				
		1	2	3	4L	4H	5L	5H	Overall
Conformation	E		0.1	0.2	0.2	0.1			0.6
	U+		0.3	1.1	1.4	0.6			3.4
	–U		0.9	3.8	6.3	3.0	0.2		14.2
	R		1.6	8.8	16.5	8.6	0.6	0.2	36.3
	O+	0.1	1.8	8.8	15.0	6.5	0.6	0.1	32.9
	–O	0.1	1.1	3.4	4.3	1.8	0.3	0.1	11.1
	P+	0.1	0.3	0.4	0.3	0.1			1.2
	–P	0.1	0.1	0.1					0.3
Overall		0.4	6.2	26.6	44.0	20.7	1.7	0.4	

Figure 2.4 Distribution of clean carcases over the classification grid, 1987.
(Source: *MLC Beef Yearbook*, 1988.)

Figure 2.4 shows the distribution of clean carcases over the classification grid in 1987. The average conformation class is R, closely followed by O+; between them these two classes account for almost 70 per cent of classified carcases. Fatness is dominated by average fat class 4L with 3 and 4H both significant. R4L is the most common single class.

Time trends shown in Table 2.6 demonstrate a gradual polarisation of conformation classes. The proportion of poor –O carcases has increased, presumably due to the Holstein effect, but so has the proportion of above average –U carcases in response to the higher proportion of continental breed crosses. The trend to better conformation is likely to become more pronounced as the proportion of purebred Holsteins slaughtered for beef declines. There is a definite trend to leaner carcases with 4L still, and likely to remain, the dominant fat class but with a declining percentage of 4H carcases and an increasing percentage in fat class 3.

The other problem which has held back carcase classification is a lack of

Table 2.6 Trends in carcase conformation and fatness.
(Source: *MLC Beef Yearbook*, 1988.)

Conformation	E	U+	–U	R	O+	–O	P
			(% of carcases)				
1984	0.4	3.7	13.1	40.6	33.3	8.0	0.9
1985	0.3	3.4	12.9	38.8	34.5	8.8	1.3
1986	0.3	3.2	12.0	37.5	35.7	10.0	1.3
1987	0.6	3.4	14.2	36.4	32.9	11.1	1.4

Fatness	1/2	3	4L	4H	5L	5H	
1984	4.0	22.9	45.1	23.5	4.0	0.5	
1985	4.4	21.8	42.9	24.8	5.3	0.8	
1986	5.5	24.7	43.9	22.3	3.0	0.6	
1987	6.4	26.6	44.1	20.6	1.9	0.4	

confidence in the consistency of application of the visual standards.

Lack of consistency is bound to be a problem with such a complicated grid and has prompted an interest in objective measurement. Probes of the type used so successfully in pig carcase classification have been tried but given that there is no smooth, firm outer skin as in the pig and that the fat layer is thinner, more uneven and softer on the hot carcase, no single probe measurement has proved as good as visual scoring in predicting carcase composition. Automatic probes in which a light beam identifies the interface between muscle and fat may be slightly more accurate and can be used to record eye muscle depth. However, it seems unlikely that probing will become the sole basis of objective classification of beef carcases.

Attention has now switched to the possibility of using velocity of sound (VOS) or video image analysis (VIA) for objective carcase classification. At the outset it must be appreciated that the high cost of electronic equipment probably limits their application to larger meat plants.

The principle of VOS is that ultrasound passes through muscle more quickly than through fat and so velocity can be used to predict carcase composition. VOS equipment has already shown its paces in live cattle evaluation and is now being tested on carcases with some promise.

VIA uses video cameras for a three-dimensional study of the carcase and its fat cover. It is potentially more valuable than VOS because it could be used for objective classification of both conformation and fatness. The evaluation of fatness is probably not very accurate because it is done by colour contrast analysis of the whitish fat and the red lean glimpsing through. Nevertheless there are already commercial initiatives in some countries to start using VIA together with fat probes for objective carcase classification.

EVALUATION OF CARCASE COMPOSITION

Carcase classification provides information on conformation and fatness which is important in its own right. It also provides an approximate prediction of carcase composition. Table 2.7 shows average percentages of saleable meat (typical commercial fat trim) over the classification grid. The values confirm the much greater influence of fatness than conformation on the percentage of saleable meat.

Once the weight, conformation and fatness of carcases are known, the only other information which improves the prediction of percent saleable beef is breed (Table 2.8). Indeed, the additional value of conformation is slight when the breed is known. The clear indication is that there would be advantages in adding breed to classification records which would not be such a fanciful idea if a national system of animal identification was developed (see Chapter 8).

There are many commercial and experimental situations where a more accurate measure of carcase composition is needed than is provided by carcase classification. The choice of method depends on the accuracy required, keeping in mind cost considerations.

Side dissection is expensive but is inevitable if it is necessary to establish base line values of carcase composition when the predictive value of indirect measures is uncertain. Once predictive relationships have been established it

Table 2.7 The relationship between carcase class and saleable meat percentage. (Source: MLC leaflet: *Selecting cattle for slaughter.*)

		Fat class				
		2	3	4L	4H	5L
		% saleable meat				
Conformation	U+	74.4	73.3	72.0	70.6	68.4
	–U	74.0	72.9	71.6	70.2	68.0
	R	73.5	72.4	71.1	69.7	67.5
	O+	72.8	71.7	70.4	69.0	66.8
	–O	71.8	70.7	69.4	68.0	65.8

Table 2.8 Prediction of saleable beef percentage.
(Source: MLC breed evaluation trials.)

	Residual standard deviation*
Weight + fatness	1.81
Weight + fatness + conformation	1.68
Weight + fatness + breed	1.45
Weight + fatness + breed + conformation	1.41

* Low values indicate the most accurate prediction

is possible to consider using much less expensive dissection of a sample joint. The rib joint is commonly used for this purpose but probably even better value for money is achieved by dissection of the thin flank (less than 10 per cent of the cost of side dissection).

For applied trials there is a lot to be said for using a commercial cutting test because it gives practical information on meat yields, joint by joint. If the test can be fitted into the routine of a cutting line at a meat plant the cost may be no more than dissecting a sample joint.

The chemical composition of meat is beginning to assume increased importance because of the concern about diet and health and the significance of this to food labelling. Chemical composition needs to be known because there is variation in the percentage of chemical fat in fat tissue.

There are many situations where it is necessary to estimate fatness or carcase composition in live cattle, e.g. the evaluation of breeding stock or the definition of slaughter end-points in experiments. For these purposes ultrasonic scanning has proved extremely useful.

Simple A-mode equipment used in pigs to bounce ultrasound off the fat/ muscle interface and project it as a spike on an oscillograph screen is not sufficiently accurate to use in cattle. However, B-mode scanners which produce a two-dimensional image of the cross section through the eye muscle give much more accurate results. The now obsolete 'Scanogram' is the best known example of a B-mode scanner but many medical scanners use the same principle.

Somewhat different in principle is velocity of sound (VOS) equipment which, instead of bouncing sound off the muscle/fat interface, passes ultrasound through the soft tissues. In recent trials VOS gave more accurate predictions of percentage fat and lean than B-mode scanners.

Originally, VOS equipment was used to pass sound through the soft tissues of the hindquarters but this is dangerously impractical working in a cattle crush. Now it has been found that sound can be passed through the loin area aiming the sound to pass between the spinous processes of the backbone. This is much more sensible but further development of VOS is necessary to make it easier to use in which case it would be the equipment of choice.

BUTCHERY TECHNIQUE

The method of butchery influences the yield of different types of cut from the carcase. In the traditional British method cuts are defined by reference to the skeleton and many muscles are cut across. In some cuts, particularly those from the forequarter, this results in a mixture of tender and tough muscles. The cut must be cooked according to the requirements of the toughest muscle.

By contrast, continental European butchers in countries such as France and Belgium have adopted a different approach in which they seam out muscles before preparing them as cuts. By this method they can take tender muscles from low value areas of the carcase and upgrade their use. The technique is applied to all muscles which can be upgraded to steak. The higher value of the cut offsets the higher labour cost of seam butchery.

Table 2.9 Comparison of traditional and seam butchery.
(Source: MLC leaflet: *Carving new markets for beef.*)

		Traditional butchery	Seam butchery
		(% of carcase)	
Carcase yield	Fat trim	8.5	12.5
	Bone and waste	20.5	20.5
	Cutting loss	1.0	1.5
	Saleable meat	70.0	65.5
		(% of saleable meat)	
Cuts	Grilling/frying	15.5	33.5
	Roasting	27.0	17.0
	Braising	32.0	16.0
	Stewing	12.0	8.0
	Dice	3.5	10.0
	Mince	10.0	15.5

The continental technique has developed against a background of butchering carcases of good conformation and the need to get from cow carcases, on which there is a high dependence, the highest possible yield of high-value cuts.

MLC butchers have adapted the continental technique for use in Britain to increase the yield of steaks from the carcase and to provide meat suitable for the preparation of value-added products. Table 2.9 shows a reduction in the yield of saleable meat but a substantial increase in the percentage of grilling/frying cuts. The values are for an R4L carcase and, whilst the implication is that the better the conformation the better seam butchery can be exploited, this has yet to be demonstrated by cutting tests.

MEAT QUALITY

People like beef very much but think it is expensive. So judged by its importance to a meal or its cost, a purchase of beef is an important shopping decision. Indifferent or poor eating quality – 'that was as tough as old boots' – has a high impact on the whole household and may divert purchases to a different butcher's shop, to other meats or to non-meat products. In view of this it is necessary to take seriously the view of many people in the meat trade who feel that the eating quality of beef is not as good as it used to be.

For all the arguments about flavour, the most likely cause of dissatisfaction with beef is toughness. The discussion of causes usually revolves around breed, sex, fatness and age at slaughter. As will be seen later, carcase handling is more important.

Differences in eating quality between breeds are remarkably small at the same carcase fatness. For example, in the MLC breed evaluation trials covering most of the popular breeds, tenderness, flavour and juiciness showed little difference in cattle slaughtered at the same fatness. In later MLC work there were only small differences between Friesian/Holstein, Hereford × Friesian and suckler-bred Charolais crosses. Sometimes when the British breeds are slaughtered at a fatter end-point than continental breeds they do have a slight edge in tenderness but this could be an effect of marbling fat (see below).

It is certainly the case that when a particular breed is associated with a quality product, e.g. Scotch beef, the whole package of breed, production system and meat handling comes together in an excellent product. This was demonstrated by MLC when Angus × heifers in a Scotch quality specification easily out-ate poor conformation Friesian/Holsteins put through a commercial specification. However, the margin of difference, though clear-cut, was not as great as many people expected.

There is no doubt that bull beef is a little tougher than steer beef, but again by a smaller margin than critics of bull beef expect. The slightly tougher characteristic is thought to be due to a higher level of insoluble collagen (connective tissue) in the muscle. On the USA 8-point scale of scoring with 8 most tender, steer beef usually scores 5.5–6.0 with bull beef about 0.5 point worse. That puts bull beef well within the range of consumer acceptance though a restaurateur seeking the ultimate in eating quality would probably avoid it.

There is a strongly held view that 'you can't have good beef without a bit of fat on it.' This school believes that the drive for leaner beef, to fit in with the campaign for healthier eating, is at the expense of eating quality. Intramuscular 'marbling' fat, in particular, is considered to have important effects on eating quality. Work in the USA supports this view and over the USDA scale of scores tenderness ratings fall sharply when marbling slips below 'slight' (about 4 per cent of chemical fat in the lean) to 'traces' or 'practically devoid.'

Slight marbling is not very much intramuscular fat but it does imply that below fat class 3 marbling is likely to be at such a low level that eating quality is put at risk.

Subcutaneous fat seems to have little direct effect on eating quality, except through its association with marbling fat. Also, through its insulating properties, subcutaneous fat may affect the rate at which carcases cool and can influence eating quality through that route. This point is considered later.

Trials in the USA have shown rather small effects of subcutaneous fat cover on steaks on tenderness and juiciness. On the other hand, MLC work with defatted topside joints indicated that the roast meat was less juicy than from conventional topside wrapped in fat.

Fat colour has relevance to the eye-appeal of beef in shop displays. Cereal beef cattle yield carcases with marble-white fat which contrasts nicely with the red of lean. Once green forages are fed the fat becomes more yellow as carotene, the precurser of vitamin A, accumulates. In cattle slaughtered at more than two years of age the yellow colouring may be strong enough to reduce carcase value. Cow carcases are the most strongly coloured, especially those from the Channel Island breeds.

The effects of age on eating quality have been studied in surprisingly few trials. Traditionalists criticise the rather pale meat from juvenile cereal beef cattle as being bland. They consider that flavour and texture are better in beef from cattle slaughtered at the upper end of the age-range. There probably are effects of age on eating characteristics but they may not be revealed by conventional taste panel scores for tenderness, flavour and juiciness.

Compared to the on-farm factors discussed so far, post-slaughter handling of carcases has far greater effects on eating quality. However, cattle handling in the immediate pre-slaughter period is also important.

Careless pre-slaughter handling of cattle on farms, in markets or at the abattoir causes stress-induced dark cutting beef. Stress uses up muscle glycogen, which is the energy source for muscular work, and reduces lactic acid production during rigor mortis. The result is meat with a high pH (over 6.0 instead of the normal 5.5) which is of dark colour, dry and of unusually firm texture. Only a proportion of muscles may be affected and the condition may not become apparent until the carcase is cut up.

This dark cutting beef, sometimes called DFD (dark, firm, dry), is not only unattractive in appearance but has a poor shelf life. Bulls are especially susceptible and the usual recommendation is that they should be loaded quietly, transported in pen groups and be delivered to the abattoir by appointment so that they can be slaughtered straight off the lorry.

After slaughter the rate at which carcases are chilled has crucial effects on tenderness. Rapid chilling can cause 'cold shortening' in which the muscles contract and set tough. However the meat is handled subsequently it remains tough. Tenderness score is reduced by a huge 4 points on the 8-point scale. As a general guide if the temperature of muscle falls below 10°C within 10 hours of slaughter cold shortening is a risk. On average, cooling rates are slower than this but carcases near the fans in a chiller may cool too fast. Ideally carcases should be left out of the chiller overnight or, failing this, chilled at 6°C for the first 10 hours. The trouble is that increasingly demanding hygiene regulations are likely to demand chilling rates which are antagonistic to final eating quality.

Carcase fat cover serves as a muscle insulator so the leaner the carcase the faster is the early cooling rate and the greater the risk of cold shortening. This by itself may explain why beef from fatter cattle has eaten better in some trials. These facts are not presented as an argument for fatter carcases but to emphasise that lean carcases must be chilled with care.

Low voltage electrical stimulation (ES) of carcases soon after slaughter accelerates muscle glycolysis and the rate at which pH declines with a reduction in the risk of cold shortening and a general improvement in meat tenderness worth about 0.5 on the USA 8-point scale of scores. However, in commercial practice responses to ES are often disappointing, suggesting that the equipment is often not used properly.

Beyond the chilling process the duration of hanging has the most important effects on the tenderness and flavour of beef. The main effect on tenderness is complete in about ten days but there are further small improvements up to two weeks which are exploited in some special quality specifications. The overall effect is a major improvement of about 3 points on the USA 8-point tenderness scale. The mechanism of tenderisation is not fully understood but involves the activity of proteolytic enzymes on the muscle fibres.

Long ago it was demonstrated that the method of suspending carcases from the carcase rail affected tenderness. The usual method is to hang the carcase from the Achilles heel. But there is an improvement in tenderness of some of the hindquarter muscles if the carcase is hung from the hip (obturator foramen). Tenderness is affected more by method of suspension than early chilling rate or electrical stimulation so it is surprising that the technique is hardly ever used.

The effects of handling on tenderness are so clear-cut that there is a strong argument for all carcases to be marked with the date of slaughter. In fact, hanging times have become shorter in recent years because meat wholesalers claim that they are short of chiller space, cannot afford the working capital to hang beef longer and cannot afford the weight loss during hanging (typically 2 per cent but sometimes higher). It is unforgivable that the eating quality of beef from cattle which have taken 12–24 months to rear should be diminished for the sake of a few days extra hanging. Fortunately, retailers are beginning to exert the pressure necessary to bring about a reform of trading practices.

It is intriguing to contemplate the development of equipment which can be used at the meat plant to check the tenderness of beef so that that any carcases which are unacceptably tough can be routed to meat manufacturing.

This discussion of eating quality has examined in turn the average effects of the various factors involved in eating quality. Of course some of them are additive and others interact. The net result is considerable variability of eating quality within which most individual factors seem rather unimportant. The upshot of this is likely to be strict quality specifications drawn up by retailers and caterers which define chilling and hanging procedures as well as carcase conformation and fatness and perhaps breed, sex and production system.

The variability in eating quality is extended by the cooking methods adopted in the preparation of the meal. Beef eats at its most tender when lightly cooked and still pink when cut – 'medium-rare' in the jargon of restaurants. However, many people prefer their beef 'well done' without realising that this makes it drier and tougher. So consumer education has an important contribution to make to good eating quality.

3 Feeds and Feeding

The ability to ration cattle to achieve required levels of performance is a precondition of planned production. Rationing depends on estimates of energy and protein requirements, the nutrient contents of feeds and feed intake.

For more than a century scientists have worked to devise systems by which cattle could be rationed. Long before that there were rules of thumb used by livestock farmers as common sayings.

Kellner developed his starch equivalent (SE) system in Germany in the early 1900s and this held sway in Great Britain until it was replaced by the metabolisable energy (ME) system in 1976. In other countries, notably in Scandinavia, the food unit (FU) system was developed. The total digestible nutrient (TDN) system developed in the USA probably owes its origins to work in Germany in the mid-nineteenth century, such is the antiquity of this field of endeavour.

All the systems have one thing in common which is that they attribute values to the nutrient contents of feeds and propose allowances for stated levels of performance. At best, rationing is an approximate business and the search is always for new systems of greater precision.

DIGESTION AND METABOLISM

The gastric stomach of the ruminant is preceded by the forestomachs – rumen, reticulum and omasum – which house the microflora and micro-fauna essential to fibre digestion.

In the rumen feed carbohydrates are fermented by microbial activity to yield volatile fatty acids (VFA), methane, carbon dioxide and microbial cells. The VFAs (predominantly acetic, propionic and butyric acids) are the main source of energy, but some starch which escapes fermentation is digested in the lower gut. So are microbial cells which are digested to yield sugars, amino acids and fat (lipid). Within the rumen there is an increase in lipid above the feed level arising from microbial fermentation of non-lipid materials.

In-feed growth promoters are available with antibacterial activity which modify rumen fermentation to cause a favourable increase in the proportion of propionic acid in the VFAs and reduce production of waste methane gas. The result is an improvement in daily gain, feed conversion efficiency or both.

Some of the feed protein is fermented in the rumen to produce VFAs and ammonia. The ammonia and its intermediate products may be incorporated into microbial protein. Alternatively, ammonia is absorbed through the rumen wall along with the VFAs, and recycled to the rumen via the saliva to have a second chance of being utilised.

The part of the dietary protein which is fermented in this way is called rumen degradable protein (RDP). Sufficient RDP is required to meet the needs of the rumen microorganisms.

About 70 per cent of the protein reaching the lower gut is microbial protein. However, there are circumstances when this is insufficient to supply the amino acid requirement of the animal. Then it is important to supply undegraded dietary protein (UDP) which escapes rumen fermentation and is digested in the lower gut. The requirement for UDP is highest in rapidly growing young cattle.

The ability of the rumen microorganisms to utilise ammonia opens up the possibility of using non-protein nitrogen (NPN) compounds such as urea as a protein source. This is certainly possible in cattle older than six months but a high energy concentration is needed in the diet for efficient urea utilisation so that the supply of ammonia arising from the rumen breakdown of urea just keeps pace with the rumen fermentation of energy.

Partition of energy

The partition of feed energy in ruminants is illustrated in Figure 3.1. Right at the outset it must be appreciated that the main destination of absorbed energy is to be lost as heat, not retained as meat.

The feed contains an amount of *gross energy* which is what would be yielded as heat if the feed was burned. Most feeds have a gross energy value of about 18.4 MJ per kg dry matter (DM) but silages average 19.2 MJ and high fat diets higher still. The energy which is digested is the *digestible energy* with the remainder voided in the faeces. Digestibility is an important measure of feed quality usually expressed as the digestibility of organic matter (D value). Part of the digested energy is lost as methane during rumen fermentation and part is lost as urinary energy. The residual energy circulating in the blood stream is the *metabolisable energy* (ME). This is the

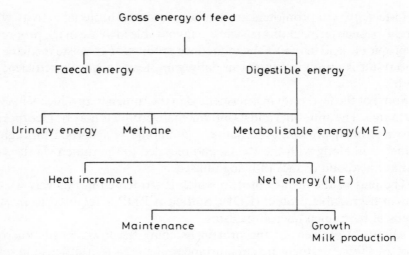

Fig. 3.1 Partition of feed energy in the ruminant.

measure of feed value used in the rationing system presented later. Metabolic work done on the ME preparing it for use in body functions results in a further loss of energy, the heat increment. The remaining *net energy* is available for maintenance, physical activity, growth and lactation.

THE ME SYSTEM OF RATIONING

The ME system of rationing was introduced in Britain in 1976 and replaced the Starch Equivalent system which had been in use since the First World War.

The ME system actually depends on estimating the net energy required for maintenance, physical activity and the amount stored in the body as meat or secreted as milk. The net energy requirement is then converted to a more convenient set of ME allowances for cattle at various levels of performance and ME values of feeds. These values, together with an estimate of feed intake can be used to design rations for stated levels of performance.

ME values of feeds

Table 3.1 shows feed values of ME expressed as megajoules per kg dry matter (MJ ME per kg DM). The table also includes values for digestibility

(D value) and protein values which will be discussed later. If only the D value of a feed is known a rough-and-ready estimate of ME can be obtained by multiplying the percentage D value by 0.15; it is not reliable for silage.

Under straws, feed values are presented for plain barley straw as grown and for straws which have been upgraded by treatment with caustic soda ($NaOH$) or ammonia gas (NH_3). The effect of treatment is partially to break down otherwise indigestible components of the cell wall structure, increasing both digestibility and feed intake. Ammonia treatment is most common in Britain and is carried out either in an electrically heated oven using 30–35 kg anhydrous ammonia per tonne of straw or in a stack of straw sealed with plastic sheeting using aqueous ammonia at an equivalent rate. Treatment cost needs to be considered very carefully in relation to the quality of the feed produced.

In a mixed ration the average ME value is referred to as M/D which is simply the total ME of the dietary components divided by the total dry matter. The trick in working out the DM value is to remember that whether it is expressed as per cent or g per kg all you have to do is to stick a decimal point in front of the figures to do the sums. So 25 per cent becomes 0.25 and 860 g per kg is 0.86. To convert fresh weight to DM multiply by the DM proportion; to calculate fresh weight from DM divide by the DM proportion.

Example:
Daily ration: 3 kg barley @ 860 g/kg DM and 12.8 MJ ME per kg DM; 20 kg silage at 25 per cent DM and 10.5 MJ ME per kg DM.
What is the M/D?

Barley: 3 kg $\times$ 0.86 = 2.6 kg DM @ 12.8 MJ ME = 33.0 MJ ME
Silage: 20 kg $\times$ 0.25 = 5.0 kg DM @ 10.5 MJ ME = 52.5 MJ ME
    Totals   7.6 kg DM   85.5 MJ ME

$$M/D = 85.5/7.6 = 11.3$$

The M/D value plays an important part in rationing because ration quality affects ME requirements. The significance of this to growing cattle will become apparent later.

Appetite

The biggest problem in devising rations for beef cattle is predicting how much feed, especially forage, they will eat.

Beef cows are generally fed rations of moderate quality and so it is

Table 3.1 Nutritive values of selected feeds.
(Source: Various including ADAS (1988) Leaflet P2087.)

Feed	Dry matter (g/kg)	Digestibility 'D' (%)
Grass silage		
High quality	250	70
Good quality	250	67
Medium quality	250	63
Low quality	250	57
Maize silage	250	67
Cereals		
Barley	860	86
Wheat	860	87
Oats	860	68
Maize	860	87
Hay		
High quality	850	67
Medium quality	850	63
Low quality	850	57
Straw		
Barley – plain	860	44
– NaOH	860	56
– NH$_3$	860	52
Wheat	860	40
Oats	860	46
Protein		
Soyabean meal (ext)	900	80
Fishmeal (white)	900	68
Protein supplement (no urea)	870	75
Miscellaneous		
Flaked maize	900	90
Molassed sugar beet pulp	870	78
Fresh brewer's grains	220	60
Roots		
Mangels	110	79
Swedes	110	82
Turnips	100	72
Fodder beet	180	70
Potatoes	210	79

Metabolisable energy (MJ ME/kg DM)	Crude protein (g/kg)	Digestible crude protein (g/kg)	Protein degradability (Low/Med/High)
11.0	175	125	H
10.5	170	110	H
10.0	165	105	H
9.0	160	100	H
11.2	70	50	H
12.8	108	92	H
13.6	124	106	H
12.0	109	85	M
13.8	98	70	M
10.0	130	77	H
9.0	100	70	H
8.0	85	55	H
6.5	40	16	—
8.3	40	16	—
7.5	90	20	—
6.1	18	10	—
6.7	50	10	—
13.4	505	455	M
14.2	701	670	L
12.0	340	305	M
14.5	110	106	M
12.5	130	79	M
11.7	245	190	M
12.4	85	60	H
14.0	95	65	H
12.7	100	70	H
11.9	70	50	H
13.3	115	80	H

probable that intakes will be less than the 2.5 kg DM per 100 kg liveweight + 1 kg DM per 10 kg milk which is the upper limit for dairy cows. Intakes tend to be slightly below the peak level in early lactation.

Intake declines sharply if low quality roughages or silages of poor fermentation quality are fed. Some specimen diets for suckler cows conforming to likely appetite limits are presented in Chapter 11.

With growing cattle age, liveweight, forage quality and the amount of concentrates fed interact to determine feed intake. On all concentrate diets intake is controlled more by the energy status of the animal than the bulk of the feed. However, on forage feeds ration quality is the key factor and generally the higher the feed rating the higher will be the feed intake.

The relationship between forage quality and intake is straightforward for hays but with silage other factors are at work. Short chopped silage is generally eaten in larger quantities than long material. Also cattle have a higher DM intake when fed drier silages made from wilted grass than when the silage is wet.

Overlying these factors is the quality of the fermentation achieved during the silage-making process. The amount of grass protein converted into ammonia (ammonia N as a percentage of total N) is the best single measure of fermentation quality. The aim should be values below 10 per cent; values over 20 per cent are bad.

With poor silages, either because of low ME or a high ammonia content, there is an increase in silage intake at least in cattle up to six months of age, if a high quality protein supplement such as fish meal is fed.

This effect of protein supplements on silage intake is the opposite of the usual response to concentrate supplements which is a depression of silage intake. The extent of the substitution is greatest on high ME silages with an average fall of 0.7 kg silage DM for each kg of concentrate DM fed. On poor quality silage the depression may be as low as 0.4 kg silage DM per kg concentrate DM.

In practice these substitution effects are somewhat unpredictable and occasionally there is no depression of silage intake when the concentrate allowance is increased. So it is important to keep an eye on silage intake, especially when concentrate allowances are changed.

Given these complex influences on feed intake it is not surprising that the prediction of feed intake preoccupies many nutritionists. Attempts to create prediction equations from an analysis of mathematical relationships between the factors involved have yielded unwieldy equations which are still not very accurate in predicting intake, especially of rations based on silage.

Here preference has been given to notional estimates of intake presented in a relatively simple look-up table (Table 3.2). Forages are differentiated

Table 3.2 Preferred values for dry matter intakes of growing beef cattle (kg).

	Grass silage[1]						Maize silage[4]		Hay			Straw
ME (MJ per kg DM):	11.0		10.0		9.0		11.0	10.0	9.0	8.0	7.5[5]	6.5[6]
Fermentation quality:	Good[2]	Poor[3]	Good	Poor	Good	Poor						
Liveweight (kg)												
100	2.6	2.3	2.4	2.1	2.2	1.9	2.7	2.5	2.3	2.1	2.0	1.8
200	4.8	4.2	4.4	3.9	4.0	3.5	5.0	4.6	4.2	3.8	3.6	3.2
300	6.6	5.8	6.0	5.3	5.4	4.7	6.9	6.3	5.7	5.1	4.8	4.2
400	8.0	7.0	7.2	6.3	6.4	5.6	8.4	7.6	6.8	6.0	5.6	4.6
500	8.5	7.4	7.8	6.8	6.9	6.0	8.9	8.4	7.5	6.5	6.0	5.1
Reduction of forage DM per kg concentrate DM	0.7	0.6	0.6	0.5	0.5	0.4	0.8	0.8	0.7	0.6	0.2	0.2

[1] Wilted, short chop silage: deduct 5 per cent for unwilted.
   : deduct 5 per cent for long material.
[2] Good fermentation: ammonia N less than 10% of total N.
[3] Poor fermentation: ammonia N more than 15% of total N.
[4] Maize silage must be supplemented with extra protein.
[5] Typical value for ammonia-treated barley straw.
[6] Plain barley straw.

according to ME value with silages subdivided into good or poor fermentation qualities based on ammonia levels. The fermentation ratings are only approximate and it should be noted that some very good silages with high protein contents can have ammonia N readings above 15 per cent. Two ME values are given for (barley) straw; the higher value should be applied to barley straw treated with ammonia.

Example:
Calculate the intake of 400 kg cattle fed 2 kg barley per day with a 10 ME, 25 per cent DM silage of good fermentation quality fed to appetite.

From Table 3.2 silage intake is 7.2 kg DM with a reduction of 0.6 kg per kg concentrate DM.

$$2 \text{ kg barley} \times 0.86 = 1.72 \text{ kg DM}$$
$$\text{Silage intake reduced by } 1.72 \times 0.6 = 1.0 \text{ kg DM}$$
$$\therefore \text{ daily intake} = \text{Barley: } 2 \text{ kg}$$
$$= \text{Silage: } 7.2 - 1.0 = 6.2 \text{ kg DM} \div 0.25 = 25 \text{ kg}$$

Rationing suckler cows

For milk production the efficiency of utilisation of ME is for practical purposes constant regardless of ration quality which makes rationing relatively simple.

Using dairy cow values the daily allowance to maintain a 500 kg cow such as a Hereford × Friesian is about 55 MJ ME; for a Blue Grey about 50 MJ ME. Cows during the last five months of pregnancy need an additional 12 MJ ME. The requirement for milk production is about 5 MJ ME per kg milk.

The main complication is whether the cow is gaining or losing weight. The discussion in Chapter 11 concludes that suckler cows should be managed to control body condition and specimen rations are presented designed to do this.

Rationing growing cattle

Rationing for growth is much more complicated than rationing the suckler cow because the efficiency of utilisation of ME varies according to ration quality (M/D). This creates a 'chicken and egg' situation where to estimate rate of gain it is necessary to know the M/D of the ration, but to know the M/D required in the ration you need to know the rate of gain.

The way round this problem is to calculate energy requirements as net energy values. Once having established the efficiency of utilisation of ME for growth in relation to ration M/D it becomes possible to estimate the net energy stored in the body at different levels of ME above the maintenance requirement. Dividing by the energy content of gains it is possible to calculate rate of gain. Then it is a relatively simple step to add maintenance and transform the whole set of requirements to more easily handled ME allowances for cattle of different weights, fed diets of various M/D values at a range of daily gains.

When the ME system was first introduced it was realised that a more sophisticated system would be needed in future taking account, amongst other things, of breed type and sex. In 1980 an Agricultural Research Council working party reviewed the ME system (ARC, *The Nutrient Requirements of Ruminant Livestock*, published by the Commonwealth Agricultural Bureau) and proposed changes including separate allowances for different breed types and for bulls, steers and heifers.

Unfortunately the working party was too academic in its approach and nine years later the recommendations have still not been implemented. One reason is that, despite the greater sophistication of ARC (1980) it is no more accurate in predicting performance than the old system. In any case events have moved on in nutrition and there is now talk of a new approach taking account of the effects of feed components such as digestible fibre and starch on the composition of gains and the efficiency of utilisation of ME.

None of this helps the farmer to ration cattle better. And worse still there is a view that because computers are so widely available there is no need to present rationing systems as simple look-up tables. This is utter nonsense! Even if farmers have computers they will probably not wish to grapple with complex rationing software which is used only infrequently.

The danger is that rationing becomes isolated as a remote computer service and is not, as it should be, part of a planning exercise which models cattle performance taking account of production targets and marketing plans as well as the feeds available. Moreover, unless the farmer is in a position to draw up outline plans he cannot get the best out of his professional adviser. Nor can he make the necessary periodic adjustments to rations which do not justify calling in an adviser.

Reluctantly the decision has been taken to use the old system of ME allowances in this book (Table 3.3). These do not differentiate breed type or sex but the important point is to take account of their effects in setting target daily gains, slaughter weights and the duration of the feeding period. Differences in feed conversion efficiency due to breed type and sex are small in effect by comparison.

Table 3.3 ME allowances for growing and finishing cattle.
(Source: ADAS (1988) *Nutrient allowances for cattle and sheep.* Leaflet P2087.)

Liveweight (kg)	M/D (MJ/kg DM)	Daily gain (kg)				
		0.4	0.6	0.8	1.0	1.2
		(MJ ME per day)				
250	8.5	45	—	—	—	—
	9.5	44	52	60	—	—
	10.5	43	50	58	67	—
	11.5	42	48	55	64	74
	12.5	41	46	53	61	71
350	8.5	57	—	—	—	—
	9.5	55	64	74	—	—
	10.5	54	62	71	82	—
	11.5	52	60	69	79	91
	12.5	51	58	66	76	87
450	8.5	68	—	—	—	—
	9.5	66	77	89	—	—
	10.5	65	75	85	97	—
	11.5	63	72	82	94	107
	12.5	62	70	79	90	103

Missing values denote requirement probably above appetite limit.

Note that for each higher increment of daily gain there is an increase in the ME requirement which reflects the higher energy content of the gains. This does not contravene the principle that overall feed conversion efficiency (ME/daily gain) is better at higher rates of gain.

There are two ways of using the table of ME allowances. One is to find out the likely rate of gain when a particular ration is fed. More important is designing a ration to support a required level of gain.

Calculating the likely daily gain is quite simple:

Example:
Calculate the daily gain of a 450 kg steer being fed a daily ration of 3 kg barley and 24 kg 25 per cent DM silage of 10 ME.

$$
\begin{aligned}
\text{Barley} \quad & 3 \text{ kg} \times 0.86 = 2.6 \text{ kg DM} @ 12.8 \text{ ME} = 33 \text{ MJ ME} \\
\text{Silage} \quad & 24 \text{ kg} \times 0.25 = \underline{6.0 \text{ kg DM}} @ 10.0 \text{ ME} = \underline{60 \text{ MJ ME}} \\
\text{Totals:} \quad & \phantom{24 \text{ kg} \times 0.25 = } 8.6 \text{ kg DM} \phantom{@ 10.0 \text{ ME} = } 93 \text{ MJ ME} \\
& \text{M/D } 93/8.6 = 10.8
\end{aligned}
$$

Look up Table 3.3 at 450 kg liveweight and, at M/D 10.5–9.3 MJ ME is just below the requirement for 1.0 kg gain per day. So, the gain will be about 0.9 kg per day.

For designing rations a novel but simple method has been adopted here which gives likely DM intake the central role it should have in the calculations.

There are eight steps in the trial and error calculation:

(1) Feed values. Use feed analysis or look up Table 3.1.
(2) M/D. Make an estimate of the likely value.
(3) ME requirement. Look up in Table 3.3 at the estimated M/D.
(4) Work out the net effect of concentrate supplementation on ME intake.
(5) See what ME intake would be provided by forage alone and decide what level of concentrate supplementation is required to make up any shortfall.
(6) Compile a trial ration and check M/D.
(7) If the final M/D is too different from the estimate, look up the ME requirement at the new M/D and adjust the ration.
(8) Compile the final ration.

Example:
Design a ration for a 350 kg steer to gain 1.0 kg per day using good quality silage (25% DM, 10 ME) and rolled barley.

(1) *Feeds*
Silage: 25% DM   10.0 ME
Barley: 860 g/kg DM   12.8 ME (Table 3.1)

(2) *Estimate M/D*
Say 11.

(3) *ME requirement*
From Table 3.3 by inspection between ME 10.5 and 11.5 the require-ment is between 79 and 82 MJ – say 80 MJ ME per day.

(4) *Concentrate substitution effect*
Barley 1 kg × 0.86 = 0.86 kg DM @ 12.8 ME provides   11 MJ
But silage reduced 0.86 × 0.6 (Table 3.2) @ 10 ME loses   5 MJ
                         Net gain in ME per kg barley fed: 6 MJ

(5) *ME from silage alone, shortfall and concentrate supplement required*
From Table 3.2 silage intake between 6.0 and 7.2, say 6.6 kg

6.6 kg DM @ 10 ME:	66 MJ
Requirement (step 3):	80 MJ
Shortfall:	14 MJ

$2\frac{1}{2}$ kg barley per day would provide an extra 15 MJ ME (step 4).

(6) *Trial daily ration*

Barley $2\frac{1}{2} \times 0.86$	= 2.2 kg	DM @ 12.8 ME	28 MJ
Silage 6.6 – (2.2 × 0.6)	= 5.3 kg	DM @ 10.0 ME	53 MJ
Totals	7.3 kg	DM	81 MJ

M/D 81/7.3 = 11.1. This is the same as estimate in step 2 so the ration is OK.

(7) *Adjust ration?*
No need.

(8) *Daily ration*

Barley: $2\frac{1}{2}$ kg
Silage 5.3 kg DM ÷ 0.25 = 21 kg

In a more complex situation with several dietary components the best approach is to equate the various components either to the forage section of the ration or to the concentrate section and include them on price preference or availability. Sometimes the estimate of feed intake will be speculative, it always is, emphasising the need to follow up the design by checking that, after a week or so to settle, the cattle eat the ration. If they do not then a new ration must be designed with a lower estimate of intake.

The eight step rationing procedure may seem rather long-winded but compared to the published system it eliminates several look-up tables. With a little practice it becomes quite quick to use. It is best not to design a single ration covering a large increment of liveweight but rather to design a series of rations each covering an increment of 50–75 kg gain.

The advisory organisations and several commercial feed companies offer a rapid computerised service which takes the sweat out of doing the calculations. But before calling them in it is well worth the effort of spending an hour with paper, pencil and calculator working out the whole winter management strategy within which the rations will be fed. Only then will the duration of the feeding period be known so that a feed budget can be drawn up to ensure that feed supplies on the farm are sufficient to carry through the feeding plan. The feed budget is just as important as the ration design. This point will be returned to in the concluding section of this chapter.

PROTEIN REQUIREMENTS

Rationing procedures have been considered in considerable detail without reference to protein. This is not to underestimate the importance of protein

Table 3.4 Undegraded dietary protein (UDP) requirements (g/day). (Source: Compiled from ARC (1984) by Miller, E.L. and Pike, I.H. (1987) *Feeding for Profitable Beef Production*. International Association of Fish Meal Manufacturers.)

Liveweight (kg)	Ration M/D	Daily gain (kg)							
		0.50		0.75		1.00		1.25	
		H × F[1]	ChX[2]	H × F	ChX	H × F	ChX	H × F	ChX
100	8	51	120	—	—	—	—	—	—
	10	73	137	99	203	—	—	—	—
	12	89	151	118	221	138	281	—	—
200	8	11	74	—	—	—	—	—	—
	10	43	100	42	147	—	183	—	—
	12	67	120	78	174	75	217	56	249
300	8	0	40	0	60	—	—	—	—
	10	21	73	0	105	0	124	—	—
	12	51	98	45	138	24	167	0	184
400	8	0	11	0	16	—	—	—	—
	10	2	51	0	70	0	75	—	—
	12	39	82	18	111	0	128	0	131
500	8	0	0	0	0	—	—	—	—
	10	0	34	0	44	0	36	—	10
	12	30	72	0	91	0	98	0	90

[1] H × F, Hereford × Friesian steers (also Charolais × heifer)

[2] ChX, Charolais cross bull (also Simmental × Limousin×)

Missing values denote requirement probably above appetite limit.

because quantity and quality are both important to cattle performance.

The understanding of protein rationing has advanced considerably during the past decade with the differentiation of rumen-degradable protein (RDP) and undegraded dietary protein (UDP).

At least 80 per cent of the crude protein in silage, barley and many protein supplements is degraded in the rumen to supply RDP which is utilised by the rumen microorganisms. Because of the importance of energy to microbial growth the RDP requirement relates directly to energy intake:

g per day RDP = 8.3 × MJ ME per day.

It is a short step to work out that a ration of 10 MJ ME per kg DM requires 83 g RDP per kg DM and that at 80 per cent degradability 83 × 100/80 = 10.4 per cent crude protein is needed to supply the RDP.

Microbial protein digested in the lower gut supplies most or all of the protein needs of older cattle but fast-growing young cattle have an additional requirement for UDP supplied direct from the feed. Fishmeal with its low degradability, high digestibility and excellent balance of amino acids is by some margin the best source of UDP, though vegetable proteins such as soyabean meal can usually supply the requirement.

The feed values in Table 3.1 show the degradability of crude protein classified as high (80 per cent plus), medium or low (under 50 per cent).

Requirements for UDP were reviewed by an Agricultural Research Council working party (ARC, 1984, *Nutrient Requirements of Ruminant Livestock*, Supplement No 1. Commonwealth Agriculture Bureau). Table 3.4 presents some of the values and demonstrates both the large differences between breed types and sex as illustrated by Hereford × Friesian steers and Charolais × bulls and the rapid decline in requirements above 20 kg

Table 3.5 Digestible crude protein (DCP) requirements for suckler cows. (Source: Adapted from ADAS (1988) *Nutrient allowances for cattle and sheep.* Leaflet P2087.)

| | Cow liveweight (kg) | | | |
	450	500	550	600
	DCP (g per day)			
Maintenance	275	300	325	345
Maintenance + pregnancy (last 5 months)	400	430	465	495
Milk yield: 60 g DCP per kg milk				
Gain: 320 g DCP per kg liveweight gain				

Table 3.6 Digestible crude protein (DCP) requirements of growing and finishing cattle. (Source: Adapted from ADAS (1988) *Nutrient requirements for cattle and sheep*. Leaflet P2087.)

Liveweight (kg)	Daily gain (kg)				
	0.4	0.6	0.8	1.0	1.2
	DCP (g per day)				
100	230	270	315	350	380
200	330	375	425	475	520
300	375	430	490	545	595
400	410	470	535	600	655
500	445	510	580	635	715

liveweight. Nevertheless, Charolais × bulls with their high rate of lean meat production still have a substantial UDP requirement at 500 kg liveweight which must be met if performance is to be sustained.

Estimates of RDP and UDP requirements made by ARC (1984) have not been turned into a practical rationing system. So there is no alternative but to use the existing digestible crude protein (DCP) system which should have been replaced by now. Nevertheless, knowledge of RDP/UDP relationships can be used for value judgments on the merits of alternative protein sources.

DCP requirements for suckler cows in Table 3.5 have been based on dairy cow values. It is important to remember that when cows are losing weight there is a negligible contribution to protein requirements but when they are gaining weight there is a DCP requirement of 320 g per kg liveweight gain.

For growing and finishing cattle Table 3.6 presents general guidelines on DCP requirements at various rates of gain. They are almost certainly underestimates for continental cross bulls at peak rates of gain.

When following the rationing procedure described earlier the DCP contribution of feeds should be totalled to ensure that they provide the requirements.

Example:
Design a ration for a 350 kg steer to gain 1.0 kg per day using good quality 25% DM silage and rolled barley.

Daily ration providing ME requirement: 2½ kg barley
21 kg silage

DCP contents from Table 3.1

$2\frac{1}{2}$ kg barley $\times$ 0.86 DM $\times$ 92 DCP = 198 g DCP

21 kg silage $\times$ 0.25 DM $\times$ 110 DCP = $\underline{578\ \text{g DCP}}$

Total: 776 g DCP

Requirement from Table 3.6:   570 g DCP

The protein effect in raising forage intake referred to previously has relevance to protein rationing. It seems to be mediated through an improvement in fibre digestion and cannot be explained entirely in terms of RDP requirement.

Protein has marked effects on the intake of low protein straws and dry season forages because it supplies the nitrogen needed to sustain microbial activity. It is to supply this requirement that blocks and licks containing urea were originally developed. Urea has no role in silage diets which are already high in NPN.

The interest in urea extends to its use as a low cost replacement for conventional protein sources. Cattle can utilise urea once they reach five or six months of age and weigh more than 200 kg.

An important thing to remember about urea is that although it has a very high nitrogen content it has no energy value whatsoever. The energy which is also needed for microbial synthesis must be supplied from another source. This is why urea blocks and liquid feeds contain a readily available energy source such as cereal or molasses; molasses is also a good source of sulphur which can be limiting in diets containing urea. Also urea is utilised best when fed little and often so is well suited to blocks and licks and to high concentrate diets fed *ad libitum*.

Urea is toxic and must be mixed into rations with care. For home mixing a dilute premix is recommended. Toxicity is at its greatest risk in the early days of urea feeding, especially if energy intake is limiting. It is advisable not to have more than 1 per cent of urea in the overall diet and protein supplements including urea rarely contain more than 4 per cent.

VITAMINS

The vitamin requirements of the milk-fed calf are just as demanding as in non-ruminants. Vitamin E is deficient in an all-milk diet which can lead to muscular dystrophy. There is an intimate relationship between vitamin E and the trace element selenium which has a narrow margin between deficiency and vicious toxicity. Milk replacers are commonly supplemented with 50 IU vitamin E plus 5000 IU vitamin D, 50,000 IU vitamin A and B vitamins.

Older cattle are largely independent of B vitamins because of rumen synthesis. However, vitamin B_{12} synthesis is impaired if cobalt is deficient. Carotene, the precursor of vitamin A, is plentiful in green feeds and cattle exposed to sunlight synthesise vitamin D. However, both vitamin A and vitamin D must be supplied to cereal beef cattle, usually via the protein supplement. The daily requirements are 250,000 IU vitamin A and 25,000 IU vitamin D.

MINERALS

Calcium, phosphorus and magnesium are the major minerals and requirements for suckler cows and growing and finishing cattle are proposed in Table 3.7.

Among the trace minerals copper is the most troublesome and deficiency occurs once the dietary concentration falls below 10 mg per kg DM (10 parts per million) in the diet. This occurs commonly on chalk, limestone and rain-leached soils. There is a serious fall in cow and calf performance which can be prevented or rectified by regular copper injections. There is a relationship between the metabolism of copper and molybdenum and on some clay soils high levels of molybdenum cause excessive copper excretion and the development of an ill thrift condition called 'teart'.

Minerals are available in a variety of proprietary forms including block licks, liquid supplements and powdered mixes. The powdered mixes are

Table 3.7 Requirements for major minerals.
(Source: Adapted from ADAS (1988) *Nutrient allowances for cattle and sheep*. Leaflet P2087.)

Suckler cows	Ca	P	Mg
Maintenance and pregnancy (g/day)	35	35	13
Milk production (g per kg milk)	2.8	1.7	0.7

Growing and finishing cattle

	Ca			P			Mg		
Daily gain (kg):	0.4	0.8	1.2	0.4	0.8	1.2	0.4	0.8	1.2
Liveweight (kg)				(g per day)					
100	14	26	37	6	10	15	3	4	5
200	17	28	38	9	13	17	5	6	7
300	21	32	42	13	17	21	6	7	9
400	25	35	46	23	26	30	8	9	10
500	27	36	46	29	32	36	10	11	12

cheapest and can be sprinkled on the feed at the barrier or mixed with the cereal/concentrate. Proprietary protein premixes contain mineral supplements.

FEEDING MANAGEMENT

Rationing is important but it is only one facet of feeding management. Profitable feeding management depends on having plentiful supplies of high quality homegrown forage, setting targets for daily gains which meet production and marketing objectives, designing sensible rations, checking that there are sufficient forage stocks to carry through the feeding plan and presenting feed to the cattle so that they have the best chance of consuming it and performing to target.

The quality of homegrown forage is crucial. High quality silage gives considerable flexibility in ration design and saves the cost of more expensive cereals. Almost invariably it pays to maximise homegrown forage in the ration. The specimen rations in Table 3.8 show just how important are the ME content and fermentation quality.

People sometimes argue that for winter store rations where daily gains are modest and for winter feeding spring calving suckler cows, lower quality silage is good enough. This argument does not stand up to close inspection. For the sake of good grassland management, especially where conservation is integrated with grazing, it is essential to aim at good silage in the ME 10 – 10.5 range. If the silage is too good for the job then it is always possible to top up the ration with barley straw.

Variation from year to year in the earliness of the growing season and rainfall lead to substantial differences in the amount of forage conserved. It is therefore important to assess whether there is sufficient feed to carry out

Table 3.8 Specimen rations for 400 kg cattle fed silage and rolled barley.

| Silage, 25% DM (MJ ME per kg DM): | | 11 | | 10 | | 9 | |
Fermentation quality:		Good	Poor	Good	Poor	Good	Poor
Daily gain (kg)				Daily ration (kg)			
0.9	Silage	30	26	25	20	25	20
	Rolled barley	—	1	2	3	$2\frac{1}{2}$	$3\frac{1}{2}$
1.0	Silage	32	23	22	18	23	20
	Rolled barley	—	2	3	4	$3\frac{1}{2}$	4
1.1	Silage	29	21	20	18	20	17
	Rolled barley	1	3	4	$4\frac{1}{2}$	$4\frac{1}{2}$	5

Table 3.9 Effects of daily gain in suckler-bred Charolais cross steers on feed requirements.

Daily gain (kg):	0.9	1.0	1.1
Daily ration (kg): silage	25	23	20
rolled barley	2½	3½	4½
Performance: start weight (kg)	350	350	350
finishing period (days)	210	175	145
slaughter weight (kg)	540	525	510
Feed budget (tonnes): silage	5	4	3
barley	0.5	0.6	0.7

the feeding plan. All too often silage runs out unexpectedly and forces expensive decisions which could have been avoided with forward planning. A feed budget – daily ration × days on feed – should always be worked out when a ration is designed.

There is scope to manipulate the level of performance of finishing cattle to match available forage supplies, and more often than not this is preferable to buying in feed or selling cattle as stores. The principle involved is that feeding for a higher level of gain reduces the daily silage intake but, more important, shortens the finishing period because cattle reach market condition sooner. In part this is because they approach target slaughter weight more quickly, and in part it is due to them finishing more quickly so that they reach the required fat class earlier, albeit at a lighter weight. Before adopting this course of action it is necessary to establish that earlier slaughter at a lighter weight fits in with buyers' requirements.

Table 3.9 shows an example of feed budgets for winter finishing Charolais cross suckler steers. Each 0.1 kg per day step up in gain saves 1 tonne of silage but increases the barley requirement by only 0.1 tonne. If forage supplies are unusually plentiful the rate of gain/rate of finishing principle can be applied in reverse again checking that cattle still meet buyers' requirements.

In most cases where daily gain is far below target, rations were either badly designed, not fed or both. Often this is because of wildly optimistic guesses about the amount of feed in a trailer load. Sometimes low and variable performance occurs because there is insufficient space for cattle at the feed barrier.

It is very important to have an idea of what 20–25 kg of silage looks like – put some in a bin and weigh it. Also ensure that stockworkers know what the daily ration is and feed it. Farmers with feeder wagons fitted with a load cell weighing system are in the best position to ration accurately but not everyone has enough cattle to justify the expenditure involved.

Many producers feed silage on the floor in front of the feed barrier and, sorting out the choicest material, cattle gradually push the feed forwards and eventually cannot reach it. As often as possible during the day the feed should be pushed back so that the cattle can feed. This is especially important when feed is distributed only once daily.

Self-feed hoppers should be inspected at least once each day to ensure that feed has not bridged in the hopper, interrupting the flow to the feed trough. Concentrate soiled with faeces or slimy with saliva should be removed.

When the cereal/concentrate is top-dressed on the silage it is important that all the cattle should be able to feed at once. Any timid feeders which cannot find space at the barrier end up as slow growers and add to the variability of performance within the pen.

If the silage and cereal are mixed, as they can be in a feeder wagon, it is not necessary for all the cattle to feed at once. Often the space at the feed barrier is cut by up to 50 per cent in this situation. Nevertheless, cattle feed most voraciously when the feed is fresh and so there are advantages in feeding twice daily if this can be fitted into the farm routine. Also, in winter, buildings need to be well lit to extend the feeding period.

Self-feeding silage direct from the face used to be popular but, as target gains for winter finishing have increased, so self-feeding has receded. The problem is that cattle have to work too hard to achieve the high intakes needed for rapid growth. In many cases a feed barrier has to be erected for feeding cereals anyway and the silage might just as well be fed there also.

4 Breeds and Breeding

The last 25 years has been a period of unprecedented breed substitution and, in many rangeland and pastoral countries, the introduction of crossbreeding systems. The next 25 years will probably be dominated by biotechnological developments in embryo transfer and genetic engineering. There is a risk of pedigree breeders being left on the sidelines unless they find ways of becoming involved in the exploitation of the new technology.

The pedigree breeder is by no means impotent in genetic improvement and the change which has been made in many breeds stands as testimony to that. Far more has been achieved than is admitted by so many geneticists whose methods of statistical analysis flatten every achievement. Nevertheless, breeders are too easily deflected from the main objectives of genetic improvement by excessive attention to fancy show points and a predilection to rustic theories.

The influence of the pedigree breeder should not be underestimated. In Great Britain, for example, about 1000 pedigree breeders produce the large majority of beef bulls used by natural service and AI for more than 2.5 million beef matings in dairy and suckler herds. The quality of the bulls has a major effect on the commercial potential of their progeny. Breeders need to recognise this and pay close attention to the needs of their commercial customers.

BIOTECHNOLOGY

Biotechnological developments in the cattle breeding sector offer two tantalising prizes. The first is the ability to clone superior embryos of known sex for transfer into recipient dams. And the second is gene transfer to introduce new genes, perhaps from another species, to produce 'transgenic' cattle which are either of improved performance or have the ability to produce novel products such as special proteins in milk.

Embryo transfer

Embryo transfer (ET) is already a well-established technique and, worldwide, probably more than 250,000 transfers are carried out annually. Usually the technique involves superovulation of a donor cow of superior genetic merit and transfer of the embryos into surrogate dams. Over the years successful non-surgical techniques have been developed for the recovery of ova from donor cows and embryo transfer (or inovulation). Recently techniques have been developed for the *in vitro* maturation of unfertilised ova, fertilisation of ova, incubation of fertilised ova and long-term storage of frozen embryos.

So far embryo transfer has been used mainly for the rapid multiplication of newly imported breeds and for obtaining additional progeny from admired females. Already exports of breeding cattle have been supplanted to some extent by the trade in frozen embryos.

Biotechnological developments offer the prospect of a completely new role for embryo transfer.

Already 'DNA probes' are available which, by recognising the Y chromosome of the XY male, can identify the sex of the embryo. Most important of all, scientists are on the verge of developing techniques for cloning sexed embryos to produce virtually unlimited numbers of identical copies for commercial use. The first calves from cloned embryos are on the ground and most workers in the field agree that cloned, sexed embryos should be available commercially by the mid-1990s.

Cloning involves the 'nuclear transfer' of the cell nucleus from a super embryo into an unfertilised ovum from an ordinary commercial cow from which the nucleus has been removed to produce a 'vacant ovum'. These unfertilised ova for nuclear transfer are collected from the ovaries of slaughtered cows. The delicate micro-manipulation involved is carried out under a microscope.

Two approaches to nuclear transfer are under parallel development. Probably the simplest in concept is to remove nuclei from cells of an early embryo at what is called the morula stage which contains 8–32 cells and forms the seven-day blastocyst which is transferred non-surgically into the recipient female (Figure 4.1).

The rate of multiplication of embryos is theoretically very rapid – using a 16-cell morula, three cycles of nuclear transer could produce $16 \times 16 \times 16 = 4096$ embryos. Rates of multiplication being achieved at present are far below this theoretical maximum.

The other approach to cloning uses stem cells of the inner cell mass of the blastocyst which develop to form the foetus (Figure 4.1). These cells are still undifferentiated, i.e. their future function has not yet been decided, so the nuclei can be used for nuclear transfer into vacant unfertilised ova. Moreover, stem cells can be cultured *in vitro* to provide an unlimited supply

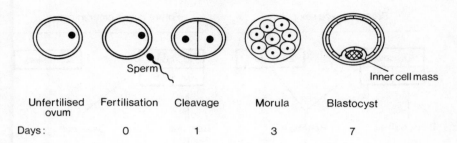

Fig. 4.1 Fertilisation and early embryonic development.

of nuclei. If this technique is successful, and it promises to be, the way is paved to large-scale commercial production of identical embryos.

In the commercially available embryo transfer services twin embryos are usually transferred into recipients. One reason is to achieve the highest possible conception rates (in theory conception rates to embryo transfer should be slightly higher than to AI). The other reason is to cash in on the higher combined value of twin calves over a single calf. Probably a third of cows inovulated with twin embryos will produce twin calves.

It is by no means certain that dairy farmers and suckled calf producers will opt for twins. Calving difficulty tends to be higher for twin than single calves, if only because the calves get tangled during parturition. Retained placentas are more common because twinning brings forward the calving date but the placenta is retained until full term. Neonatal mortality is higher for twin than single calves. Rebreeding tends to be delayed after a twin calving and there may be a reduction of milk yield in the dairy cow. And finally, with the lighter twin calf slightly poorer rearing performance is likely than from the single calf.

Researchers rightly point out that when a twin pregnancy has been identified, correct feeding of the cow and careful supervision at calving should eliminate most of the problems. But more work is needed to demonstrate a clear advantage to twinning.

Embryo transfer has a potentially important role in genetic improvement programmes through the multiple ovulation and embryo transfer (MOET) technique described later. But cloning *per se* adds surprisingly little to rates of genetic progress. Nevertheless it could be used to improve the accuracy of estimates of breeding value, to test cattle in different management systems and to test carcase quality and eating characteristics by slaughtering some cloned cattle before large-scale cloning for commercial use. Cloning really comes into its own in commercial cattle production and could transform the structure of the cattle industry.

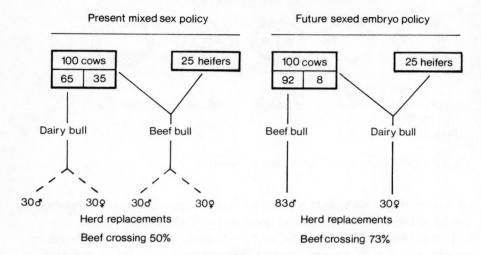

Fig. 4.2 Probable effect of sexed embryos on the breeding strategy in dairy herds. (Assumption: 90 calves per 100 cows.)

When sexed clones become available a commercial dairy farmer, for example, would probably use his first calving heifers to carry most of the replacement female embryos. The heifers would have the easiest possible calving because of the light birthweight of female calves. This would leave most of the easier calving cows to carry male purpose-bred beef embryos. The effect of this strategy would be to raise the level of beef crossing from the present maximum of 50 per cent to over 70 per cent (Figure 4.2). And as a corollary the purebred Friesian/Holstein bull calf would be eliminated from commercial beef production which would please the meat trade.

It is easy to see the new technology being taken up by dairy farmers but less certain to what extent it would be used in suckler herds where easy care is usually a priority. Perhaps the chance to increase the proportion of bull calves would persuade some suckled calf producers that it is worth modifying management during the mating period to make embryo transfer possible.

With embryo transfer in suckler herds it would be possible to use suckler cows bred solely for maternal characteristics – fertility, ease of calving, milk yield – and to transfer into them embryos bred for terminal sire performance – growth, feed efficiency, carcase yield and meat quality.

What suckled calf producers will almost certainly not do is to employ the breeding strategy that optimises biological efficiency which is a once-bred heifer system. Female embryos are transferred into heifers which are slaughtered after a short suckling period in an all female system (see Chapter

11). The practical management problems of once-bred heifer production transcend the theoretical advantages.

The other route to sex control is via sexed semen. Over the years there have been many false claims of success. It is not clear whether any laboratory has a major programme on sexing semen because confidentiality is paramount in an area where the financial rewards of success are so huge. With modern cell-sorting techniques or the possibility of using immunological methods there must be hopes of differentiating sperm into its male (Y chromosome) and female (X chromosome) components. If and when a technique is developed, even one giving partial control of the sex ratio, it is possible that farmers would prefer the simple AI route to more complicated embryo transfer.

This is an appropriate moment to stress that realising the full potential of these new techniques depends on the genetic quality of the stock being used. There is no point in cloning run of the mill embryos. So testing programmes are necessary in which the performance of clones is checked, from ease of calving, through growth rate and feed efficiency to carcase and meat quality before mass cloning takes place. Moreover, embryo production needs to be backed up by breeding programmes which achieve high rates of genetic progress for the objectives of key economic importance.

Gene transfer

Potentially the most powerful method of manipulating performance is by gene transfer. Laboratory techniques exist for the isolation of a gene, its modification, multiplication and incorporation into the nucleus of an early embryo of the same or a different species. The transferred gene may become incorporated into the genotype and the animal is described as transgenic.

The understanding of gene transfer is as yet rather primitive and, while transgenic mice have been produced which grew to twice the size of normal mice, few transgenic farm animals have been produced and usually their performance has not come up to expectations.

Future progress depends on identifying genes of major importance and then on a better understanding of how to control the expression of genes. Then gene transfer could be used to improve performance by increasing growth hormone secretion, to increase disease resistance or to modify milk secretion in dairy cows so that, for example, they synthesise human proteins making the milk more suitable for feeding to babies.

Revolutionary technologies such as these bring their own problems. People do not like the idea of food or farm animals being 'tampered with'.

The arguments in favour of exploiting biotechnological advances will be hard won because even the technical jargon – embryo transfer, clone, transgenic – is consumer unfriendly.

And, finally, there is the question of breeders' rights and patents. When an embryo is cloned should the original breeder receive royalty payments? The battle for royalty payments to breeders for bulls in AI was lost years ago. And what are the patent rights for transgenic animals? The answers are of crucial importance to private breeders and breeding companies alike because they influence investment policies.

For further reading on biotechnological developments the reader is referred to Woollams, J.A. and Wilmut, I. (1989) *Animal Production*, **48**, 3–30.

BREED CHOICE

Differences in performance between breeds are such that breed substitution is far quicker as a way of changing the level of cattle performance than selection within a breed.

The history of breed development is accompanied by numerous breed substitutions. Bakewell's Longhorns were replaced by the Shorthorn which was itself replaced by the Hereford for beef and the Friesian for milk. Now continental breeds, particularly Charolais, Limousin and Simmental, have largely supplanted the British beef breeds. And the Holstein from North America has penetrated deeply into the European race of Friesians.

The latter period of intense breed substitution in Britain which began with the importation of the Charolais in 1961 is now nearing its conclusion. The only imported breeds to have recent impact are the double-muscled Belgian Blue and Piemontese.

Breed comparisons

Running parallel with active breed substitution has been a worldwide programme of experimental breed comparisons. There is now good information on the basis of which breeds can be fitted into production systems.

Various aspects of overall breed performance are important to different sectors of the beef industry and consumers. The calf producer is very concerned about ease of calving, calf viability and juvenile growth. The finisher wants fast growth, efficient feed use and good carcase quality. The meat trader looks for carcases in the preferred weight range of good shape, not too fat and with a high yield of saleable meat and a high proportion of high-priced cuts. And the consumer wants value for money and good eating satisfaction.

There are trade-offs right along the line. The heavier breeds which grow fast and use feed efficiently cause a higher level of calving difficulty and more calf mortality than smaller breeds. The lean breeds which produce the type of beef demanded by health-conscious consumers can have such a low level of marbling fat that eating quality is diminished.

The ensuing discussion is largely about terminal sire performance, i.e. the bulls used to sire the slaughter generation. The analysis of breed effects on maternal performance is included in Chapter 11 on suckled calf production. Suffice it to say here that the hybrid vigour (heterosis) of crossbred females brings important improvements in reproductive efficiency and calf viability. Hybrid vigour effects on growth are small and on carcase quality even smaller.

Sire breed effects on dystocia are similar in dairy and beef suckler herds. The MMB survey results in Table 4.1 show a considerable advantage in ease of calving and calf mortality to the medium-weight native British breeds. Gestation lengths were greater for the continental breeds, especially Blonde d'Aquitaine and Limousin. Early results for the double-muscled Belgian

Table 4.1 Sire breed effects on dystocia in Friesian/Holstein dairy herds. (Source: Milk Marketing Board.)

Dam	Sire breed	Serious difficulty (%)	Calf mortality (%)	Gestation (days)
Friesian/Holstein heifers	Angus	2.3	5.8	—
	Friesian	7.4	7.9	—
	Hereford	3.1	6.2	—
	Limousin	8.1	9.7	286
Friesian/Holstein cows	Belgian Blue	4.3	5.4	284
	Blonde d'Aquitaine	3.4	4.8	289
	Charolais	4.2	5.2	285
	Chianina	6.1	6.5	286
	Friesian	2.5	5.0	281
	Hereford	1.2	2.9	283
	Limousin	3.2	6.1	288
	Simmental	3.1	5.6	286
	South Devon	2.4	5.6	285

Table 4.2 Dystocia in commercial suckler cows.
(Source: MLC.)

	Assisted calvings (%)	Calf mortality (%)
Charolais	9.6	4.8
Simmental	9.3	4.2
South Devon	7.4	4.1
Limousin	7.2	4.4
Lincoln Red	5.4	3.0
Devon	5.6	2.6
Hereford	3.8	1.6
Sussex	3.4	1.5
Angus	3.1	1.3

Blue show an incidence of calving difficulty similar to the Charolais. In the MLC calving surveys in suckler herds, assisted calvings (a lesser grade of difficulty than the MMB serious difficulty rating) and calf mortality were closely related to the size of the sire breed (Table 4.2).

British farmers have come to terms with the higher incidence of difficult calvings caused by the heavy continental breeds. They are still anxious about heifer matings, though many farmers are quite prepared to use breeds of intermediate calving difficulty such as the Limousin. But for cow matings, dairy or beef, the continental beef breeds – Charolais, Limousin, Simmental, etc. – are preferred. The cost of supervising more difficult calvings is more than offset by the greater value of the calf.

The higher birth-weight of calves sired by the heavy continental breeds (which is the main cause of higher calving difficulty) is the first signal that the growth potential of the calf is greater. The effect of sire breed on preweaning growth in suckler herds is demonstrated well by MLC results from commercial farms (Table 4.3). The results also show that, while the ranking of sire breeds is the same in lowland, upland and hill herds, the margin of superiority of calf weight declines as the environment deteriorates.

When the results for dystocia are combined with those for calf weaning weight it becomes apparent that, despite the greater dystocia, the heavy sire breeds generate greater total annual productivity per cow (Table 4.4). This is why so many commercial suckler herd owners have switched to continental breed sires.

Differences in preweaning gain are carried through into the finishing period. Allied to differences in earliness of maturity the differences in gain lead to considerable differences between breeds in age and weight at slaughter and total feed consumption. This is ably demonstrated by results

Table 4.3 Effect of sire breed on calf 200-day weight in commercial suckler herds. (Source: MLC.)

Sire breed	Type of herd:	Lowland	Upland	Hill
		Calf 200-day weight (kg)		
Charolais		240	227	205
Simmental		232	222	198
South Devon		231	221	200
Devon		225	215	191
Lincoln Red		222	214	189
Sussex		215	207	186
Limousin		215	204	186
Hereford		208	194	184
Angus		194	182	176

from the MLC breed evaluation programme in which the cattle were all slaughtered at fat class 4L (Table 4.5). Companion carcase results were presented earlier in Table 2.2.

Late maturing Charolais crosses were considerably older and heavier at slaughter than Angus crosses. The Charolais crosses had a higher daily feed consumption to fuel the 10 per cent higher daily gain. Because of the longer finishing period total feed consumption was much higher for the Charolais crosses but feed efficiency was similar to Angus crosses.

A feature of key importance in the results is the effect of size and earliness of maturity on feed consumption illustrated by the Angus/Charolais comparison. Big late-maturing Charolais crosses ate much more feed in total than smaller, early maturing Angus crosses. Being bigger and growing faster they ate more per day, and being later maturing they had to be fed longer. However, the extra feed was just about balanced by extra production so that there was little difference in feed efficiency. It is worth noting here that, while there is little difference in feed efficiency between breeds, there is important variation within breeds.

Broadly similar results were obtained in companion MLC trials evaluating the performance of dairy breeds and crosses (Table 4.6). Cattle were reared in two production systems, one equating roughly to the 18-month beef system and the other to grass beef in which cattle are finished off grass following a winter store period.

The added ingredient in the dairy beef results is that the Friesian and (Canadian) Holstein both used their feed less efficiently than all the beef breed × Friesians. The reason for this was the combination of very late

Table 4.4 Calculated annual productivity of lowland suckler cows mated to different sire breeds.

Sire breed	Assisted calvings (%)	Calf mortality (%)	Calving interval* (days)	Weaning weight (kg)	Weaning weight/ cow/year (kg)
Charolais	9.6	4.8	375	240	222
Simmental	9.3	4.2	375	232	216
Limousin	7.2	4.4	376	215	200
Hereford	3.8	1.6	372	208	201
Angus	3.1	1.3	370	194	189

* Taking account of gestation length and the delay in rebreeding after an assisted calving.

Table 4.5 Comparative performance of suckled calves in winter and summer finishing.
(Source: Southgate, J.R., Cook, G.L. and Kempster, A.J. (1982) *Animal Production*, **35**, 87–98.)

Sire breed*	Start weight (kg)	Slaughter age (days)	Daily gain (kg)	Slaughter weight (kg)	Daily feed (kg)	Total feed (kg)	Feed efficiency (kg feed/kg gain)
(a) Winter finishing							
Angus	319	477	0.77	393	8.9	927	11.6
Charolais	363	520	0.84	494	10.2	1520	12.1
Devon	328	494	0.78	419	8.9	1094	11.4
Hereford	322	492	0.78	410	8.8	1066	11.3
Limousin	332	517	0.78	454	9.2	1348	11.8
Lincoln Red	336	489	0.85	428	9.6	1121	11.3
Murray Grey	324	493	0.68	405	8.6	1046	12.6
Simmental	359	517	0.86	490	10.2	1486	11.9
South Devon	335	517	0.77	451	9.2	1342	11.9
Sussex	324	512	0.76	428	8.9	1255	11.7
(b) Summer finishing							
Angus	317	505	0.96	408	10.1	967	10.5
Charolais	355	570	1.07	525	11.1	1775	10.4
Devon	339	518	1.00	444	9.9	1086	9.9
Hereford	328	527	1.00	442	10.0	1176	10.0
Lincoln Red	352	520	1.05	465	10.9	1196	10.4
Simmental	352	572	1.08	526	11.4	1860	10.6
South Devon	342	551	1.06	488	10.8	1513	10.2
Sussex	334	538	1.03	461	10.2	1306	9.9

* Mated to Hereford × Friesian and Blue Grey dams.

Table 4.6 Comparative performance of dairy-bred calves in 18-month and grass beef production.
(Source: Adapted from Southgate, J.R., Cook, G.L. and Kempster, A.J. (1988) *Animal Production*, **46**, 353–364.)

Breed/cross	Slaughter age (days)	Daily gain (kg)	Slaughter weight (kg)	Daily feed*	Total feed (t)	Feed efficiency (kg DOM/kg gain)
(a) 18-month beef system						
Friesian (F)	523	0.83	466	4.8	2.0	5.8
Holstein	589	0.82	522	5.0	2.5	6.1
Charolais × F	526	0.92	519	4.8	2.1	5.2
Hereford × F	450	0.83	399	4.2	1.5	5.1
Limousin × F	516	0.83	459	4.3	1.8	5.2
Lincoln Red × F	447	0.87	423	4.4	1.6	5.1
Simmental × F	527	0.88	491	4.5	1.9	5.1
South Devon × F	494	0.81	440	4.3	1.8	5.3
Sussex × F	448	0.87	409	4.3	1.5	4.9
(b) Grass beef system						
Friesian (F)	768	0.67	559	4.7	3.2	7.0
Holstein	814	0.70	619	4.9	3.6	7.0
Charolais × F	772	0.75	627	4.7	3.2	6.3
Hereford × F	714	0.66	515	4.2	2.6	6.4
Limousin × F	760	0.72	587	4.4	2.9	6.1
Lincoln Red × F	717	0.67	515	4.3	2.7	6.4
Simmental × F	744	0.72	581	4.5	3.0	6.3
South Devon × F	715	0.73	560	4.4	2.7	6.0
Sussex × F	735	0.69	541	4.2	2.7	6.1

* kg digestible organic matter (DOM)

Table 4.7 Number of cattle of different breeds/crosses needed to produce the same slaughter weight in 18-month beef.

	No. of cattle to produce the same slaughter weight
Friesian (F)	1.00
Holstein	0.89
Charolais × F	0.90
Hereford × F	1.16
Limousin × F	1.02
Lincoln Red × F	1.05
Simmental × F	0.95
South Devon × F	1.06
Sussex × F	1.14

maturity with moderate daily gains which resulted in a long feeding period.

Results for the Angus × Friesian were not included in the analysis of results. Early in the trial Angus × Friesians were similar in daily gain to Hereford × Friesians and even earlier maturing with a slightly lower slaughter weight.

It is important to remember that added to these differences in cattle performance there are important variations in killing-out percentage and meat yield (see Table 2.1) which favour the continental breed crosses but are unfavourable to the Holstein.

The commercial beef producer needs these comparative results for two purposes. Firstly, to evaluate the price that can be paid for different breed types. And secondly, to plan the production system so that breed/cross is exploited to the best advantage.

Standards of performance for the main breeds and crosses are presented in the later chapters on production systems. However, it is worth noting here just how much breed influences the planning of the beef system. As an example, Table 4.7 shows the effect of breed/cross on the number of cattle needed to produce the same output of slaughter weight.

Complementarity

What has become apparent from the world-wide trials is that no breed or group of breeds is likely to top the profit league over the whole range of production systems. Variations in growth rate and earliness of maturity are best exploited by using breed types in production systems to which their performance characteristics are complementary. Breed complementarity is equivalent to 'horses for courses' in racing.

Earliness of maturity in particular has fundamental effects on the way in which breed types fit into beef systems. The interaction between earliness of maturity and diet quality is most important of all.

Early maturing breeds such as Angus and Hereford were developed to cope with prolonged and severe winter store periods and to produce beef from low quality feeds. On these feeds late maturing Charolais crosses would grow bone and some muscle but would not finish and would develop the appearance of store cattle. So a finishing ration for an Angus cross could be a store diet for a Charolais cross!

At the other end of the scale, high quality rations which exploit the rapid, lean growth of Charolais crosses would cause Angus and Hereford crosses to become overfat at excessively light weights.

Between these extremes there are many middle quality diets which can be used to produce beef from both early and late maturing cattle. It is a relatively simple matter to adjust numbers to the feed available taking account of slaughter age and weight.

Earliness of maturity assumes critical importance when there is seasonal variation in feed quality and availability. Grass finishing illustrates very well the issues involved.

A production model for dairy-bred steers in a grass beef system is presented in Table 4.8. There need be no difference between breeds in gain per hectare provided stocking rates are adjusted for the weight of cattle. However, the different types vary in the time it takes them to reach market condition which favours the early maturing cattle.

The short grazing period of early maturing Angus and Hereford × Friesians is an advantage because slaughter commences in mid-grazing season and reduces cattle numbers nicely in step with declining grass production as the season progresses and the quantity and quality of grass decline. There is also a younger generation of cattle on the farm and the slaughter of finished cattle releases grazing for them as their requirements

Table 4.8 Production model for grass finishing dairy-bred steers.

	Angus × Friesian	Hereford × Friesian	Friesian/ Holstein	Limousin × Friesian	Charolais × Friesian
Daily gain (kg)	1.0	1.0	1.0	1.0	1.1
Grass finishing period (days)	110	120	170	190	170
Slaughter weight (kg)	450	475	550	575	610
Grazing stocking rate (cattle/ha)	5.1	4.8	4.3	4.2	3.9

increase through the season. So all-in-all performance matches the seasonality of grass production very well.

Late maturing Friesian/Holstein, Limousin × Friesian and Charolais × Friesian steers are used in the system but are not so well suited to it. The long grass finishing period makes it difficult to sustain high daily gain from mid-season unless concentrates are fed. As a result a proportion of cattle fail to finish off grass and must be yarded in the autumn for finishing on winter diets or a further store period. Worse still, the older cattle compete increasingly with the younger cattle as the season progresses and performance is put at risk.

These late maturing types perform to better advantage when they are used in production systems with higher rates of lifetime gain on all-concentrate or silage/cereal rations where there is no seasonal restriction on duration of the finishing period.

A rather different conclusion emerges from an analysis of grass finishing suckler-bred stores. This is partly because there need be no younger cattle on the farm at the same time. Also, because suckler-bred cattle are at least three-quarters bred to beef breeds, even the Charolais cross is earlier maturing than the ultra-late Charolais × Friesian.

The production model in Table 4.9 for grass finishing uses Hereford-crosses and Charolais-crosses as examples of early and late maturing types.

Hereford crosses are so early maturing that the main consideration is how best to organise a second finishing batch to utilise all the grass grown. The usual method is to have two overlapping batches, replacement cattle being purchased as those from the first batch are slaughtered. Cattle in the second batch perform slightly less well because of lower grass availability and quality from mid-season.

The longer grazing period for Charolais crosses means that a single batch utilises all the grass grown. Slaughter reduces cattle numbers fast enough to keep step with declining grass production. In many respects the later maturing cattle fit grass finishing better.

Table 4.9 Production model for grass finishing suckler-bred stores.

| | Hereford × | | Charolais × |
	First batch	Second batch	
Daily gain (kg)	1.0	0.9	1.1
Grass finishing period (days)	100	90	165
Slaughter weight (kg)	475	450	550
Grazing gain (kg/ha)		775	775

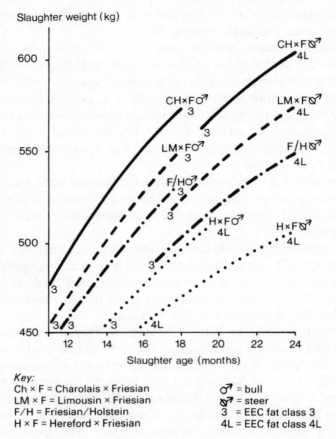

Fig. 4.3 Relationships between slaughter age, slaughter weight and carcase fatness in dairy-bred steers and bulls.

These two grass finishing examples show how important it is to fit breeds and crosses into systems of production which suit them. There is no doubt that complementarity is a key factor in breed choice.

What happens in practice is that producers adjust breed performance through the rations they feed and by modifying slaughter end-points within the range acceptable to buyers. This results in characteristic relationships between slaughter age, slaughter weight and carcase fatness of the sort shown in Figure 4.3 for dairy-bred steers and bulls.

Crossbreeding systems

The foregoing discussion has taken no account of the breeding systems needed to produce crossbreds. In Great Britain crossbreeding is such an integral part of the cattle industry structure that it is hard to imagine why crossbreeding is not exploited in the same way everywhere.

In some situations crossbreeding is not used at all. In France, for example, there is some terminal sire crossing in dairy herds and in the rustic mountain breeds, but the major lowland breeds such as Charolais, Limousin and Blonde d'Aquitaine are bred pure. The potential advantage of hybrid vigour for improved reproductive performance is rejected in favour of the simplicity of a purebreeding system.

The same argument was used for years in rangeland and pastoral countries where there are still many herds of purebred cattle. However, in these countries farmers exploit increasingly the use of terminal sire breeds to improve growth rate and carcase quality and crossbred cows for better reproductive efficiency.

The two best-known crossbreeding systems for use in self-contained beef herds are criss-crossing and rotational crossbreeding. Criss-crossing is the simplest, making alternate use of two sire breeds. More complicated, but giving greater flexibility, is rotational crossbreeding usually using three breeds in sequence, sometimes more.

In a stable criss-crossing system the proportion of blood of the two breeds alternates between two thirds and one third in succeeding generations. A rotational crossbreeding system with three breeds holds the maximum contribution of each breed at around 55 per cent. In both crossbreeding systems it is an advantage if the breeds used are of similar performance.

BREED DEVELOPMENT

In essence, breeding better cattle is a simple matter of defining objectives, recording performance, using the records to select superior breeding stock and minimising the generation interval by giving preference to young cattle in breeding programmes. Unfortunately all too often objectives are confused, performance records are inaccurate, breeding stock selection is compromised by over-attention to peripheral issues and old favourites are retained long after they have been outclassed by younger cattle. Moreover, practical breeders are completely nonplussed by the complex statistical methods used by geneticists, few of whom have the common touch to describe in layman's terms the conclusions of their sophisticated calculations.

Selection objectives

Defining objectives is the first job and the list is a long one including fertility, ease of calving, calf survival, milk yield, growth rate, feed conversion efficiency, carcase quality and hard-wearing qualities of the jaw, limbs, feet and udder.

Such a long list presents problems because the more objectives there are in a breeding programme, the less genetic progress can be made for each of them. So a serious attempt must be made to simplify objectives to offer a real chance of genetic progress. Simplification is made more difficult by the antagonisms between desirable objectives. In general maternal objectives are opposed to terminal sire objectives.

There is certainly no room for misplaced objectives such as the compact cattle theory which bedevilled Hereford breeding in the USA during the 1930s and led to a dangerous increase in the frequency of dwarfing genes. Nor is there room for the showring preoccupation with perfect conformation which is perpetuated from show to show, country to country.

A major issue in the simplification of objectives is whether a breed should specialise or pursue a 'middle of the road' policy. The cost of specialising but getting it wrong is obscurity. This is a real risk when selection decisions today do not bear commercial fruit until a decade later. The cost of a middle course is a lack of high-powered performance for any single characteristic. What cannot be excused is the casual claim made by some breeders that there are strains within the breed to suit every need without giving commercial buyers a clue as to how to select cattle with the characteristics they need.

It is, however, valid to consider whether different objectives should be set in breeding bulls for crossbreeding in suckler herds from those used in dairy crossing. The answer is probably not because breed choice gives the flexibility required. However, selection within breed does come into play and what happens in practice is that suckled calf producers, conscious of growth performance, buy bulls of high weight-for-age, while dairy farmers, concerned about ease of calving in heifer matings, take the lighter bulls.

Probably the best guide is to concentrate on overall fitness – the ability to survive and reproduce – in adverse environments which are very hot or very cold, very wet or very dry as this focuses most attention on maternal performance. Specialisation should be reserved for the terminal sire breeds whose main use is to sire the slaughter generation of calves. Then the main emphasis can be on growth and carcase quality.

Heritability is a measure of the proportion of the total variation in performance among cattle which can be attributed to their complement of genes (genotype). The rest of the variation is due to environment – feeding,

Table 4.10 Preferred values of heritability.

	Heritability (proportion)
Fertility	0.10
Calving difficulty	0.10
Calf survival	0.05
Birthweight	0.40
Weaning weight	0.25
Yearling weight	0.40
Feed conversion efficiency	0.40
Conformation score	0.50
Fat thickness	0.30
Saleable meat	0.40
Functional soundness	0.50
Milk yield	0.25
Temperament	0.50

climate, disease, etc. The higher the heritability the greater is the influence of genotype on overall performance (phenotype) and the faster the potential rate of genetic improvement. Preferred values of heritability are given in Table 4.10 for the main performance characteristics (traits). These are controlled by large numbers of 'additive' genes. A few characters such as colour, horning and double-muscling are controlled by single 'major' genes or small groups of genes.

Weight-for-age, feed conversion efficiency, carcase composition, conformation and functional soundness and temperament all have moderate to high heritabilities and so selection would be effective. On the other hand, fertility which also has a high economic value has a low heritability. Whilst breeders may find it hard to accept that fertility does not respond much to selection it becomes easier to understand once it is realised that cattle which are infertile or die eliminate themselves from the population thereby over many generations reducing the amount of genetic variation. Then most of the variability which remains is due to environmental factors.

In the same vein it is important to distinguish between repeatability and heritability. As an example, it is possible to rate AI bulls on ease of calving and, knowing that the rating will apply to future matings, to avoid bulls causing high levels of difficulty with large effects on average calving difficulty. Nevertheless, the heritability of calving difficulty is low and so the response to selection is small.

Fortunately, characters of low heritability exhibit the greatest hybrid vigour or heterosis when breeds are crossed. This results in an expression of performance above the average of the parent breeds, often higher than either breed. This is the phenomenon which makes crossbred cows so superior to purebreds in lifetime performance.

In the end every discussion about cattle breeding comes back to conformation. Geneticists cannot understand why so much attention is paid to a character which they consider to be, at best, of minor importance. But breeders themselves believe that conformation is all-important, though fashions do change.

The discussion in Chapter 2 concluded that at a given carcase fatness the better the carcase shape the slightly higher the percentage of saleable meat. So good conformation is an advantage. But good conformation needs to be defined with care. The search for smooth, blocky conformation which obsessed breeders of the native British breeds through the 1950s and 1960s tended to fill in the hollows with fat so that overall fatness increased and the percentage of saleable meat declined. On the other hand, better conformation achieved by thicker muscling improves the yield of saleable meat.

The ultimate end-point in selecting for extreme muscling is the double-muscled 'Culard' which has an exceptional percentage of lean. A comparison of normally-muscled and double-muscled Belgian Blue cattle in Table 4.11 illustrates the point. However, the overall performance of double-muscled cattle is often so poor that in many countries double-muscling is regarded as a genetic defect. Belgian Blue breeders have overcome their most pressing problem – calving difficulty – by the expedient of routine use of Caesarean section for calving. There is a view that such an approach cannot be supported because it contravenes good cattle welfare.

A reasonable attitude to conformation would be to set growth standards first and, only when these have been met, to take account of shape. Happily, many breeders have reached this position already.

But the showring lags behind and far too many judges are unskilled at judging carcase merit in live cattle and set breed type above important considerations such as temperament and structural soundness. There is a

Table 4.11 Comparison of normally-muscled and double-muscled Belgian Blue. (Source: Hanset, A. (1987) *British Cattle Breeders' Club Digest*, **42**, 35–44.

	Normal	Double-muscled
Killing-out (%)	60.0	64.8
Seventh rib:		
lean (%)	58.7	70.5
bone (%)	19.2	16.7
fat (%)	22.1	12.8

strong case for live/dead training courses for judges to give the showring, and more particularly the pre-sale show, greater commercial relevance. Shows could and should be more than beauty contests.

An important selection issue associated with conformation is how best to manipulate earliness of maturity. There are great differences in appearance between the muscular late maturing Charolais and the early maturing

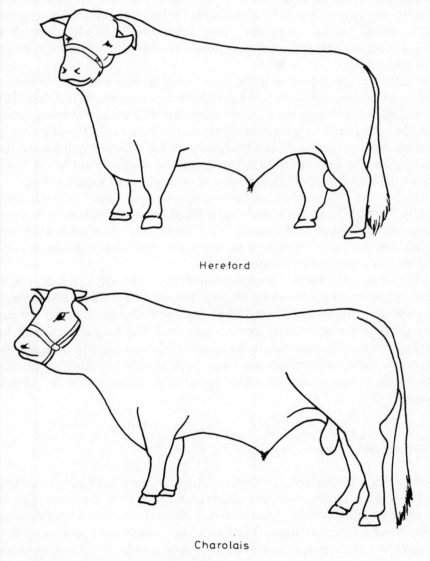

Hereford

Charolais

Fig. 4.4 The appearance of contrasting breeds.

Hereford (Figure 4.4). A natural supposition is that selection for higher daily gain would lead inevitably to later maturity. Certainly this would be the trend but daily gain and later maturity are not inexorably intertwined. The selection for greater weight-for-age in the Angus, for example, is not turning the breed into a black Charolais.

This is an important point because there are obvious advantages in selecting for faster growth. However, for reasons of complementarity with production systems, it may be undesirable to shift earliness of maturity too far. In reality, the rate of genetic change, even in a well-ordered breeding programme, is slow enough for earliness of maturity to be kept under continuous review.

Related to this discussion is the USA frame score which seemed at one time to be gaining hold in Britain but happily now seems to be receding. The proposition is that taller cattle with higher frame scores are heavier, leaner and can be finished to a greater slaughter weight. In the USA frame score has become such an obsession that the tallest, lankiest cattle regularly win the steer shows. For a time in Britain it looked as though prices at Hereford bull sales would become more closely related to height than weight-for-age.

Much of the USA research on frame scores is ill-founded. Often the cattle with higher frame scores are continental breed crosses, and those with lower scores are British breeds. Naturally, the continental crosses are heavier and leaner. The fundamental error is to take these between-breed comparisons and draw a within-breed conclusion.

Of course, taller cattle are on average heavier but why estimate weight from height when cattle can be weighed just as easily? There is no reason whatsoever, why, within a breed, the taller cattle should be leaner. In any case, the proper way to assess fatness is by trained handling or better still, by ultrasonic scanning. And finally, frame score takes no account of muscularity which from earlier discussion has been shown to influence carcase composition. As a concept frame score should be consigned to the rubbish dump.

Recording and testing

Having established selection objectives, the next step is to employ recording and testing procedures which measure performance for the estimation of breeding values. Accuracy, speed and cost all need to be taken into account.

Breeding value is estimated directly and potentially most accurately by a progeny test of the performance of calves produced from random matings. For maternal characters and for a detailed evaluation of carcase and meat

Table 4.12 Comparative accuracies of performance and progeny testing.

Heritability (proportion)	Performance test	Progeny test			
		10 calves	20 calves	40 calves	80 calves
		Accuracy 0–1 (perfect)			
0.2	0.45	0.58	0.72	0.82	0.90
0.4	0.63	0.73	0.83	0.91	0.95
0.6	0.78	0.80	0.88	0.94	0.97

quality a progeny test or sib test must be used. But progeny testing is slow because of the time it takes to produce and rear calves and can only be applied to a limited number of sires because of the expense and practical limits to facilities and the number of cows available for test matings.

Fortunately for characters such as growth the animal's own performance (performance test) is a guide to breeding value which is quicker and cheaper than progeny testing. The comparative accuracies of performance and progeny testing in Table 4.12 show that the lower the heritability the more progeny testing comes into its own. But even then it is not until more than 10 progeny per sire are tested that there is a real improvement in accuracy over performance testing.

Breeders prefer progeny testing because it leads to fewer mistakes. The trouble is that in so many herd tests there are two few progeny for an accurate result and the test is compromised because matings are not at random. The outcome is that the progeny test results are no more accurate, sometimes less accurate, than a performance test the results of which could have been available three years earlier. In any case the key decisions taken by breeders relate to the selection of young cattle as herd replacements.

Speed is important because of the significance of generation interval (the average age of parents at the birth of the calf) to genetic progress. The measure that matters is not progress per generation but progress per year. In other words progress per generation must be divided by the generation interval. The performance test may be less accurate than progeny testing but a breeding programme using a succession of young bulls will make faster annual progress than one based on older progeny-tested bulls.

This is not to argue that progeny testing has no place. Remember that all breeding programmes produce calves and progeny records. Using the top 10 per cent of progeny-tested sires adds to genetic progress in a breeding programme based on performance testing. Also, for AI sires progeny testing is worthwhile for ease of calving, growth and carcase quality because even a small genetic advantage is multiplied many times when the sires are used for mass breeding in commercial herds.

Herd recording

Almost all beef improvement programmes are founded on a herd recording system. For example, in the MLC scheme ease of calving is scored and calves are weighed at birth and then four times a year until about 18 months of age. Weights are adjusted to the nearest 100-day point. Particular attention is paid to 100- and 200-day weights as indicators of milk yield in the dam and to 400- and 500-day weights as indicators of the genetic potential for gain. A high proportion of pedigree breeders in Britain participate in the MLC scheme.

There is considerable variation in weight among cattle around the breed averages (Table 4.13) giving considerable scope for selection. Heifer weights are lower than those for bulls because of the moderate nutrition during rearing which is consistent with optimum lifetime performance. Nevertheless, 400- and 500-day weights are still useful for selecting heifers with the best growth potential.

The simple records can be used to produce a sophisticated analysis of herd performance including rankings of bull and heifer calves, lifetime analysis of cow performance and cow rankings and sire progeny test results.

There are two problems in the interpretation of herd results. In the first place pedigree beef herds are on average far too small (Table 4.14) for accurate comparisons of cattle within the herd. And secondly, variations in management from one herd to another bedevil comparisons of cattle from different herds. What tends to happen in practice is that breeders sweep these problems under the carpet and compare cattle on their absolute weight records, a highly misleading practice. Worse, it encourages breeders to feed bulls to achieve the highest possible weight-for-age without proper regard to sound management or future use. The best advice to buyers is to look for bulls which are above their herd average weight at 400 or 500 days of age.

The first step in unravelling the problem of interpreting records is to recognise the non-genetic factors at work which influence performance. These include the sex of the calf, its season of birth, the age of its dam and whether or not it was creep-fed. Traditionally there have been two ways of handling the records. In the USA correction factors have been used to adjust records to a common base. So, for example, weaning weights of calves born to dams two years old are multiplied by 1.15 to make them equivalent to

Table 4.13 Breed average weights, 1986–88.
(Source: *MLC Beef Yearbook*, 1988.)

	Bulls					Heifers	
Age (days)	100	200	300	400	500	400	500
			Weight (kg)				
Angus	129	233	343	458	560	337	384
Beef Shorthorn	137	252	349	455	552	355	407
Blonde d'Aquitaine	155	269	390	519	652	386	462
Charolais	175	319	463	615	740	447	513
Devon	134	228	323	448	537	305	364
Hereford	136	240	350	463	558	343	397
Limousin	154	275	402	533	632	394	448
Lincoln Red	146	248	366	501	552	342	na
Murray Grey	136	237	330	442	536	326	381
Simmental	175	312	451	591	699	423	483
South Devon	159	283	408	549	680	392	457
Sussex	135	233	343	454	550	337	397
Welsh Black	139	230	331	453	na	324	367

na: not available.

Table 4.14 Size distribution of pedigree beef herds recorded by MLC, 1988. (Source: *MLC Beef Yearbook*, 1988.)

	No of herds	No of cows:	1–20	21–40	41–60	61–80	81+	Average herd size
			% of herds					
Angus	39		50	31	10	3	6	28
Belgian Blue	15		93	0	7	0	0	11
Blonde d'Aquitaine	27		82	14	0	0	4	14
Charolais	197		76	18	6	<1	<1	16
Devon	17		35	36	17	6	6	34
Hereford	69		45	32	13	7	3	33
Limousin	215		79	17	3	<1	<1	15
Murray Grey	12		42	50	8	0	0	20
Simmental	338		80	9	1	<1	<1	11
South Devon	54		42	39	15	2	2	28
Sussex	16		44	38	6	6	6	31
Welsh Black	12		25	17	50	0	8	44

calves from five-year-old dams. The disadvantage of this method is that it applies a breed average correction factor to a particular herd where relationships may be different.

In the MLC scheme a contemporary comparison approach has been preferred. Records are still corrected for age of dam but thereafter the analysis is based on contemporary calves of the same sex, season of birth and preweaning management. The disadvantage of this approach is that in small herds (and bigger herds with year-round calving) there are too few contemporaries for accurate comparison.

BLUP

Advances in statistical methods and computer technology offer a new approach to the analysis of breeding records. Most important is the elegant but highly complex statistical procedure developed by Professor Henderson in the USA called BLUP (best linear unbiased predictor). Cleverly, this uses all the records from similar environmental groups and from related pedigree groups (sires, dams, sibs, grandparents) to calculate more accurate estimates of breeding value.

Not only is BLUP a more accurate method of handling herd records but, provided there are related cattle across herds, it can be used to estimate breeding values for cattle from different herds which can be compared directly, herd effects having been accounted for.

The original versions of BLUP were highly complex and, even analysing records for a single performance character, could bring the biggest computer to its knees. Now with the development of BLUP techniques and the falling cost of computer power, it has become possible to run BLUP for several performance characters at once on quite small computers. Indeed, some versions will run on the modern generation of personal computers.

Essentially what BLUP does is to differentiate genotype from environment in the formula:

Phenotype = Genotype + Environment

What it cannot overcome is the intrinsic problem of the small herd. Nor can BLUP scan across herds properly unless there are sufficient related cattle linking the herds together. Most studies of herd pedigrees have revealed a surprising number of related cattle in different herds even when natural mating prevails. But herd links can still be greatly improved by the use of AI reference sires. Reference sire schemes exist in Australia, France, New Zealand and the USA and are useful for progeny testing against a common base whether or not BLUP is used to analyse the results (see Breeding Programmes, later).

Performance testing

The most common method of obtaining comparable estimates of breeding values for bulls from different herds has been to performance test them at central stations. There bulls are given standard management so that performance can be compared directly. Also, at a central station it is possible to employ more comprehensive measurement procedures such as individual feeding.

Herd management effects before tests start are still a problem because they carry over into test performance. The older the bull at the start of test the worse these carry-over effects become. For bulls eight months old at the start of test or older, pre-test effects are so firmly imprinted that the ranking of bulls on weight at the end of test is so similar to rankings at the start that it is fair to argue that the test was a waste of time.

Geneticists are quite clear that bulls should be as young as possible when the test starts, certainly not more than three months of age. However, in trials they have failed to demonstrate satisfactory performance in bulls weaned at such an early age. Conversely, breeders argue against tests starting before bulls are at least seven months old. They know that growth is enhanced by a longer suckling period and have good practical reasons for avoiding early weaning because they are left with the problem of drying off the cow.

Reactions to the problem vary. In France and the USA there is little concern about age at the start of test and bulls can be up to 10 months old when they enter test stations. In the USA a warm-up period of at least three weeks precedes a daily gain test lasting about 140 days. Pre-test effects are rampant. At the other extreme continental European tests of dual purpose breeds start when the bulls are only a few weeks of age following artificial rearing. Even this early start does not eliminate pre-test effects entirely because it has been demonstrated that milk feeding levels in the first week or so of life have long-lasting effects on growth. Also, growth is affected by prenatal influences which cannot be eliminated.

The MLC approach in Britain was to start central tests at 150–190 days of age, allowing a fairly normal suckling period but hopefully limiting pre-test effects. Examination of results from these tests in which bulls were offered a high quality feed *ad libitum* suggests that pre-test effects did not have the damaging carry-over effects on test performance that occur in tests starting at an older age.

The MLC central test stations were closed in 1986 because of escalating costs and falling demand, in favour of on-farm testing with most of the measures of the central test. Because pre-test effects are similar for bulls within a herd, age at the start of test is not so critical. However, some on-farm tests are cooperative involving bulls from different herds and then pre-test influences need to be taken into account.

One disadvantage of the switch from central stations to on-farm testing has been the loss of individual feeding except on a few farms. The consequences of this are discussed later.

At one time there was considerable controversy over whether tests should end at constant age or constant weight and, if at constant age whether 400 or 500 days was most appropriate. In fact it does not matter because in the large majority of tests the same bulls would top tests at both ages.

Breeders used to argue that tests should continue until 500 days of age to identify bulls which 'grow on' to the high mature weights they admire. There seems no good reason for this addition to test duration and cost. For one reason, bulls rank much the same at 400 and 500 days. And, in any case, bulls which are rapidly approaching maturity – the 'stoppers' – can usually be picked out by their above average backfat readings.

It is significant that since on-farm testing came into vogue the argument for longer tests has receded. If anything, breeders would like tests to end sooner so that below average bulls can be slaughtered for bull beef while they are still in the preferred weight range set by meat buyers.

Test duration needs to strike a balance between what is suitable for practical management and knowledge that the heritability of daily gain increases as the test period lengthens. On balance, test periods should not be less than five months, preferably longer.

Related to the question of test duration is which measure of growth should be used in the estimation of breeding values. The convention in the USA is to use daily gain whereas in most other countries weight-for-age is the criterion. In Sweden an index has been devised using both daily gain and weight-for-age.

Daily gain is suspect as the measure of growth because pre-test effects are mediated through daily gain on test. Often there is a negative relationship between pre-test gain and test gain because bulls whose growth has been held back by poor pre-test management exhibit compensatory growth on high quality test diets. The warm-up period in USA tests is not long enough to overcome this effect. Weight-for-age is the end result of the various influences at work and is preferred as the measure of growth performance.

Table 4.15 shows a selection of results from MLC on-farm performance tests and demonstrates the usual wide range of performance.

Table 4.15 MLC on-farm performance test results, 1987–88.
(Source: *MLC Beef Yearbook*, 1988.)

	No. of test groups	400-day weight (kg)		Ultrasonic backfat (mm)		Muscling score*	
		Mean	Range	Mean	Range	Mean	Range
Angus	7	493	347–657	4.6	1.9–8.5	12.9	9–14
Charolais	17	636	468–772	2.6	1.5–4.1	13.3	11–15
Devon	5	463	354–555	4.6	2.6–8.4	10.7	7–15
Hereford	12	495	326–697	4.2	1.3–9.3	11.1	8–14
Limousin	42	543	394–702	2.6	1.0–5.3	13.3	10–15
Simmental	23	634	456–746	3.3	1.5–6.2	13.1	11–15
South Devon	9	584	379–816	3.1	1.5–5.5	11.8	9–15

* On a scale 1 poor to 15 excellent.

Selection indices

Genetically the most efficient way of computing performance test results is as a composite selection index compiled from the records of performance rather than evaluating the various performance records one at a time.

A selection index uses all the performance records relevant to the stated objective and takes account of variability within the test group, heritabilities, phenotypic and genetic relationships (correlations) between characters and financial values of components of the objective.

The MLC Beef Index of terminal sire performance has the stated objective 'to improve the financial margin between the value of saleable meat and the cost of feed taking into account the cost of difficult calvings'. Index scores are calculated from records of calving difficulty score, birthweight, 200- and 400-day weights, daily feed intake, muscling score and (ultrasonic) fat thickness.

Some important measures of performance are not included in the MLC Beef Index and must be evaluated separately. These include structural soundness and temperament. Maternal ability is best dealt with in a separate cow index using records of calving interval and calf weaning weight.

The variability of performance is measured by the statistical term 'standard deviation' (Figure 4.5). A third of cattle have performance

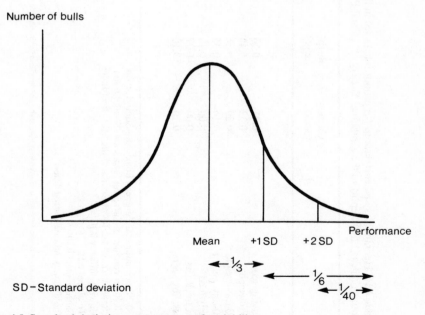

Fig. 4.5 Standard deviation as a measure of variability.

Table 4.16 Heritabilities and correlations (as proportions) used in the MLC Beef Index.
(Source: Allen (1987) Report to the Zimbabwe Society of Animal Production.)

	Calving score	Birth-weight	200-day weight	400-day weight	Daily feed	Fat thickness	Muscling score
				Genetic correlations (above diagonal)			
Calving score	**0.01**	0.50	0.20	0.10	0.00	0.00	0.10
Birthweight	0.33	**0.40**	0.40	0.40	0.10	-0.07	0.20
200-day weight	0.20	0.36	**0.25**	0.60	0.50	0.00	0.20
400-day weight	0.10	0.35	0.72	**0.40**	0.70	0.30	0.25
Daily feed	0.00	0.10	0.42	0.63	**0.40**	0.15	0.20
Fat thickness	0.00	-0.27	0.32	0.23	0.37	**0.30***	0.00
Muscling score	0.10	0.10	0.25	0.25	0.10	-0.10	**0.20****
				Phenotypic correlations (below diagonal)			

*　0.10 for continental European breeds and South Devon
** 0.30 for continental European breeds and South Devon
Preferred heritabilities for objectives of the MLC Beef Index:
　Calving difficulty 0.10
　Total feed 0.50
　Saleable meat 0.40
　(bold figures indicate **Heritabilities**)

Table 4.17 Characteristics of bulls with high and low MLC Beef Index scores. (Source: *MLC Beef Yearbook* (1988).)

	Calving score	Weights			Backfat	Muscling score
		Birth	200 days	400 days		
		(Standard deviations on a scale +3 to −3)				
Scores of 120 points or more						
Angus	0	+0.4	+0.9	+1.4	−0.5	+0.5
Charolais	0	+0.5	+1.2	+1.2	−0.7	+0.9
Hereford	+0.1	+0.4	+1.1	+1.2	−0.5	+0.7
Limousin	0	+0.2	+1.0	+1.3	−0.5	+0.8
Simmental	0	+0.6	+1.0	+1.2	−0.4	+0.5
Scores of 80 points or less						
Angus	0	0	−0.3	−0.5	+1.5	−0.5
Charolais	+0.7	−0.8	−1.1	−1.2	+0.4	−0.6
Hereford	+0.4	0	−0.9	−0.8	+0.7	−0.4
Limousin	+0.6	−0.4	−0.9	−1.0	+0.6	−0.6
Simmental	+0.8	−0.1	−0.8	−0.9	+0.2	−0.5

between the mean and one standard deviation (SD) above. A sixth of cattle are more than one SD above the mean and only a fortieth more than two SDs above. As an example, the SD of Hereford 400-day weight is about 65 kg. In the presentation of MLC Beef Index results deviations are presented within a scale of +3 to −3.

Reliable estimates of heritabilities and phenotypic and genetic correlations are hard to come by but preferred values used by MLC are presented in Table 4.16. Note the lower heritability of fat thickness and higher heritabilities of muscling score adopted for the lean muscular breeds.

Financial values (economic weights) are used in selection index designs so that scores express the greater profitability of superior performance. It surprises many people to find that these financial values can be varied over quite a wide range without much effect on index scores. Nevertheless, some breeds may have good reason for attaching a higher financial value to a particular aspect of performance, e.g. calving difficulty. So different selection index designs may be appropriate for different breeds.

The MLC Beef Index scores bulls from 50 points (poor) through 100 (average) to 150 (excellent). The standard deviation of scores is 20 points so a third of bulls would be expected to score 100–120 points and only one in six over 120 points. Table 4.17 shows that high scoring bulls are easily calved, fast-growing, lean and well-muscled.

Calculations show that in each increment of genetic progress worth £1 an increase in the value of saleable meat is the main component offset by the cost of higher feed intake with neutral or slightly beneficial effects on calving difficulty (Table 4.18).

Earlier it was mentioned that in on-farm performance tests individual

Table 4.18 Financial components of genetic progress using the MLC Beef Index. (Source: Allen (1987). Report to the Zimbabwe Society of Animal Production.)

Index design:	Angus	Hereford Red breeds	Limousin Blonde d'Aquitaine South Devon	Charolais Simmental
	Components of £1 increase in value (£)			
Calving difficulty	0.00	0.02	0.10	0.10
Total feed intake*	−0.27	−0.27	−0.26	−0.19
Saleable meat	1.27	1.25	1.16	1.09
Totals	1.00	1.00	1.00	1.00

* Negative value indicates an increase in feed intake

Table 4.19 Relative accuracy of records in the MLC Beef Index
(Source: Allen (1987). Report to the Zimbabwe Society of Animal Production.)

Index design:	Angus	Hereford Red breeds	Limousin Blonde d'Aquitaine South Devon	Charolais Simmental
		Relative accuracy (%)		
Basic records*	65	59	65	71
Basic records:				
+ birthweight	66	65	72	74
+ feed	82	81	84	95
+ fat	93	94	87	86
Basic records:				
+ birthweight + feed	82	83	88	96
+ feed + fat	98	100	100	100
+ birthweight + fat	95	94	87	86
Complete records	100	100	100	100

* Calving score, 200- and 400-day weight, muscling score

feed intakes are not usually recorded. This raises the question of what effects missing records have on the accuracy of the selection index. Table 4.19 shows that in addition to the basic pedigree records (calving score, 200- and 400-day weight, muscling score) fat thickness and daily feed are the most important measurements. Feed intake is particularly important in the Charolais design and emphasises the desirability of recording individual feed intakes, if only for part of the test.

Heifers are not usually reared in a formal performance test but they are almost always reared as a single management group so it is well worthwhile compiling their pedigree records as index scores to assist in the selection of herd replacements.

Progeny testing

When top bulls from performance tests go into the AI stud there is a strong case for a progeny test to validate the performance test estimate of breeding value and to get a rating of calving difficulty.

All AI beef bulls should be progeny tested for ease of calving. In breeds which are used for both heifer and cow matings there is a case for testing both types of mating in case ratings vary. The records include gestation length, calving difficulty scored at various levels of severity and neonatal calf mortality. Results are collected by postal survey and it requires 200 calvings to be surveyed in order to achieve, for example, the modest precision which differentiates bulls 3 percentage units apart in serious calving difficulty.

There have been few trials to check whether a performance test rating of beef bulls bred in a suckler herd environment gives a good estimate of breeding value when the bulls are used for crossbreeding in dairy herds to produce calves which are artificially reared and used for dairy beef production. Such results as there are show rather a poor relationship between the performance test and progeny test results.

The usual reaction to these negative results is to cast doubts on the accuracy of performance testing procedures. This may often be the case but progeny test procedures may also be at fault. Or it may be, as is often the case in genetic studies, that much larger scale trials are needed for conclusive proof. One problem of working with selected AI sires is that the predicted range of progeny performance is small in any case. To do the job properly would need a large number of top and bottom bulls from performance tests. Such a trial is unlikely to go ahead given the present state of research funding.

The main routine programme of beef progeny testing in Britain is carried out by the Milk Marketing Board at its Warren Farm testing centre. Bulls are crossed with Friesian/Holsteins and about 25 test calves per bull are purchased and reared in a grass/cereal beef system with slaughter at about 18 months of age. Progeny test reports present results for daily gain, slaughter age and carcase gain per day. To be really useful meat yields from the carcase need to be measured in these tests.

An alternative to station progeny testing is to locate calves in commercial beef units. The variation in management from farm to farm gives the results particular commercial relevance and the capital cost of a testing station is saved. However, control is more difficult and inevitably there is a loss of records. It is therefore necessary to increase the number of calves purchased from each bull to at least 30 for a test of acceptable precision.

The advent of cloning will bring new opportunities in testing. It will become possible to generate a limited number of cloned embryos to produce calves for testing before mass cloning is undertaken. The calves could be tested in a variety of beef systems as a check on complementarity and measurements can be carried right through to the eating quality of beef.

Breeding programmes

Selection is all-important because it is the power the breeder has over cattle for genetic improvement. Breeding values are only as good as the use made of them for selection.

The most serious limit to what can be achieved in beef breeding is the small average size of most breeding herds. The accuracy of estimated breeding values is low because there are so few contemporaries. And opportunities for selection within the herd are limited because of the need to control inbreeding at a low level. In many herds this means that all replacement bulls must be purchased.

Inbreeding can be a problem in bigger herds too unless mating plans are drawn up to avoid closely related cattle. Failure to do so risks inbreeding depression which is the opposite of hybrid vigour and causes a decline in reproductive performance and calf viability. Moreover, lethal and crippling recessive factors are exposed as pairs of 'recessive' genes come together. The 'bulldog calf' is an example of a lethal recessive, happily now rarely seen. When unrelated cattle are mated one of the genes making up the pair is more likely to be a 'dominant' gene and the undesirable condition is subdued.

The best general guide is to avoid matings between cattle which have more than one common grandparent or are even more closely bred. The rule may be relaxed from time to time to mate together cattle of exceptional performance. A simple measure of the rate of inbreeding in a large closed population is one over eight times the number of sires used each generation. The aim should be to hold the rate of inbreeding below 0.5 per cent per annum.

The all-round advantages of bigger herds – more accurate estimates of breeding values, higher selection intensity and easier control of inbreeding – add up to a considerable advantage. Figure 4.6 shows that a 100-cow herd can make genetic progress 75 per cent faster than a 15-cow herd. Beyond 100 cows diminishing returns set in and the 150-cow herd has a rather small advantage over 100 cows, though the breeding programme is much easier to organise. Really it is not until herd size reaches 75 cows that it becomes possible to contemplate an independent breeding programme.

In a large herd using natural service the top 10 per cent of performance-tested bulls would be retained and the best 50 per cent of heifers. Each young bull would be mated to at least 15 females. There are genetic advantages in bringing back into use the top 20 per cent of bulls with the best progeny test results. However, practical problems of 'laying-off' bulls until their progeny test results become available may be insuperable. There are also potential genetic advantages in reserving 10–15 per cent of matings for sampling the best bulls from the rest of the breed, either by purchasing young bulls from time to time or, preferably, by the use of AI sires. Most breeders would find the heavy dependence on young bulls in such a breeding programme alien to their usual practice.

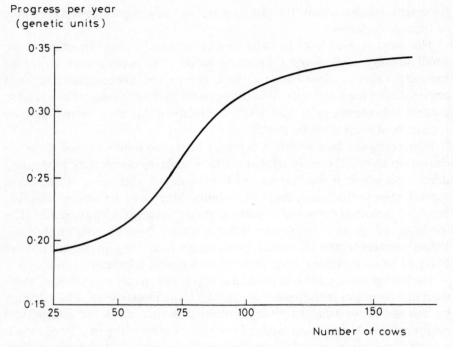

Fig. 4.6 Effects of herd size on rate of genetic progress.

For female selection in the large natural service herd the argument for rapid generation turnover used for bulls does not apply. This is because the balance of increasing accuracy of estimating breeding value as the cow bears more calves offsets the greater generation interval. The optimum number of calvings is 5–6. Indeed, it could be argued that as long as a cow can get into the selection zone of the cow ranking list she should be retained regardless of her age.

Smaller herds can contribute to genetic progress by participation in cooperative schemes which make effective herd size larger. An example of cooperation which can work breed-wide is provided by young bull proving schemes operated by MLC in cooperation with breed societies. These schemes take top young performance testing bulls and use them by AI in breeders' herds. This spreads their influence and enables them to be progeny tested. Semen is stored so that bulls with the best progeny test results can be re-used. Even the smallest herds can participate but, because of the shortage of contemporaries, records from these herds make little contribution to the progeny test result.

Young bull proving schemes provide a good example of the extent to which genetic progress is dominated by the young bulls. If the top 1 in 10 young performance-tested bulls are selected and the top 1 in 5 progeny-tested bulls are re-used, then 90 per cent of the genetic progress attributed to bulls comes from the young bulls and only 10 per cent from the progeny-tested sires.

As another example of cooperation, in medium and large-sized herds the reference sire system can be used to create genetic links between herds. Usually, reference sires are used in progeny tests of home bred bulls to allow results to be related to a common base so that bulls tested in different herds can be compared directly. The most common problem is that the reference sires are not used for sufficient matings within each herd for the genetic links to be accurate. French researchers have calculated that at least 15 progeny by reference sires are needed if three homebred bulls are being progeny tested and 25 reference progeny if a single homebred bull is being progeny tested. In response to this the French system spreads the progeny tests over two years as a way of cutting down the number of reference sire matings.

Since the reference sires account for a large number of matings, the standard of their selection is critical. There is always the danger of compromise committee decisions which result in the reference sires being of moderate performance. Then they do more harm than good.

The problem with broadly-based schemes is gaining sufficient allegiance from individual breeders for the genetic potential to be realised. Loyalty is best when a group of like-minded breeders come together out of a desire to do better than they can when working alone. The breeders' groups pioneered in Australia and New Zealand are a good example of this.

The best arrangement is a group breeding scheme in which the participating breeders each contribute cows to a central nucleus herd. If the best cows from the satellite herds are contributed to the nucleus there is a lift in genetic merit of the nucleus which gets it off to a flying start. The nucleus is used as the focus of careful recording and testing and uncompromising selection of young bulls and female replacements. The opportunity to measure performance more accurately and to collect additional records, e.g. individual feed intake, can really add to the rate of genetic progress. Satellite herds take their replacement bulls from those bred in the nucleus and play a multiplying role.

There has been considerable genetic planning work on the optimum design of group breeding schemes. A major issue is whether the nucleus should be 'open' and take a proportion of its female replacements from the satellite herds or whether it should be 'closed'. At first sight an open nucleus is attractive because it allows top females identified in the satellite herds to join the nucleus. In reality this can be counter-productive because testing and selection are so rigorous in the nucleus that apparently good females from satellite herds are brought down to earth when they have to compete in the nucleus. Conversely there is always a case for sampling bulls from other herds to see how they compare with nucleus stock; they also help to keep inbreeding at bay.

Breeders' groups have not had much impact in Europe. One reason is the high capital cost of setting up a nucleus herd. Nevertheless looser groupings still have merit and it is worth noting that a breeders' group cooperating to performance-test bulls at a central location and sharing the use of top young bulls in their herds could aspire to achieve 80 per cent of the rate of genetic progress of a full nucleus herd scheme.

Breeders forming a group must consider financial matters as well as genetic objectives. An important benefit of grouping is that it allows greater attention to publicity, more organised marketing of breeding stock and a better after-sales service than an individual breeder could contemplate. Short-term these commercial advantages are likely to outweigh genetics in importance. Therefore it is essential that the constitution of the group and its business arrangements are drawn up with care.

In the last few years geneticists have made new proposals on the design of breeding programmes exploiting multiple ovulation and embryo transfer (MOET) which demand a complete realignment of thinking on cattle breeding.

MOET can so increase the reproductive rate of females that a breeding programme can be devised in which intense selection and rapid generation turnover can be combined to make genetic progress potentially a third faster than in the best conventional breeding programme. With improved MOET techniques even faster progress may be possible in future.

A programme for a terminal sire breeding programme using a herd of 150 commercial recipient cows might be operated as follows:

(a) Transfer selected pedigree embryos into 150 commercial recipients with the production of, say, 120 calves.
(b) Performance test 60 bull and 60 heifer calves.
(c) Select the top 6 bull calves (10 per cent).
(d) Select the top 12 heifer calves (20 per cent).
(e) Multiple ovulate the heifers and mate with the young bulls to produce 10–15 embryos per heifer.
(f) Transfer the embryos into 150 commercial recipients.
(g) Sell all the parent bulls and heifers.

In this programme there are no cows, no selection for maternal performance and no sire progeny testing. MOET increases the selection intensity which can be applied to females and reduces the generation interval from the conventional five years or more down to three or less.

MOET is much more complicated to operate than a conventional breeding programme and is much more expensive. It is significant that the few existing MOET schemes in Britain are hosted by institutional organisations and the only commercial programme, for Friesian/Holsteins, was purchased recently by the Milk Marketing Board. Nevertheless, it is probable that as cloning is exploited commercially, embryo production companies will want the production of parent stock supported by MOET programmes operated by themselves or in cooperation with private breeders. Breeders need to seize this opportunity.

It is fitting that this section on breeding programmes should end with considerations of commercial viability because there is no sense in breeding cattle of the highest genetic merit while becoming bankrupt in the process.

DUAL TESTING FOR MILK AND BEEF

In many parts of the world, and certainly throughout much of Europe, the dairy breeds perform a dual role producing beef as well as milk. It is natural that dual testing programmes for milk and beef should have been established in many countries for breeds such as the Friesian and Simmental. Usually the dairy progeny test is preceded by a beef performance test.

The possibility of dual testing in the Friesian/Holstein breed in Britain has been discussed sporadically for the last 20 years. Most of the model calculations concluded that, since dairy responses to selection were financially more valuable than beef responses, there was no case for reducing the selection pressure for milk and, at best, there was only a marginal case for dual testing.

However, against a background of penetration of the British Friesian population by extreme dairy Holstein blood and growing complaints from the meat trade about the poor conformation of Friesian/Holstein carcases, in 1978 the Milk Marketing Board introduced beef shape scores into dairy progeny test reports. The scores were awarded to heifer progeny during the routine inspection for dairy type. Trials showed that the beef shape scores of sires were correlated with the carcase conformation of steer progeny and the weight of lean produced. There is no culling of bulls on the basis of beef shape scores. However, there is some evidence that dairy farmers prefer to nominate bulls which combine good dairy ratings with high beef shape scores.

The imposition of milk quotas in 1984 changed the basis of calculations on dual testing. It coincided with the possibility of using MOET to increase the number of calves produced by dairy bull mothers so that beef testing need not reduce the selection pressure for dairy merit. In this situation joint studies by MMB and MLC concluded that using MOET dual testing would be cost-effective.

However, it should be pointed out that the beef testing was only expected to slow down the rate of deterioration of beef merit, not reverse it.

The deterioration is a manifestation of the negative relationships which exist between beef characteristics (notably beef shape) and milk, fat and protein yields. In a mixed Friesian and Holstein population the negative correlations are in the range –0.3 to –0.5. Moreover, in response to milk quotas the level of beef crossing in dairy herds has increased from 35 to 50 per cent. Also, since 1989 the EEC system of supporting beef prices in the UK has changed and there is no longer the severe penalty of loss of subsidy payments on carcases of poor conformation, though there are still price penalties in the market place. All of these factors weaken the case for dual testing.

Looking ahead the prospect of being able to clone embryos of predetermined sex will make dual testing irrelevant. Then dairy farmers would produce sufficient purebred dairy females for herd replacement and mate the rest of the herd to produce beef-bred calves. The level of beef crossing would increase to 70–75 per cent and the purebred male Friesian/Holstein could virtually disappear from beef production. The only sector which would be affected by the extreme dairy shape of the Friesian/Holstein would be the cull cow market.

5 Planning and Financial Management

The underlying theme of this book is that a high standard of technical performance is the route to profitable beef production. In no sense does this undermine the key importance of planning and financial management to ensure that the beef enterprise has the profit potential to be exploited by good technical performance.

Beef is commonly a secondary enterprise, on lowland farms to arable cropping and on upland farms to sheep. But invariably the beef enterprise ranks high in its requirement for working capital. This makes good financial planning all the more important.

When drawing up the plan the first requirement is that the beef enterprise should fit individual farm circumstances. It may be needed to use land not good enough for more profitable enterprises or to utilise the grass break in an arable rotation. On arable farms the availability of crop by-products for feeding may be a factor or the cattle may use spare labour in the winter. In this situation there is a temptation to overvalue farmyard manure as a fertiliser or to justify cattle for non-profit reasons because they add interest to the day-to-day running of the farm.

Sometimes a beef enterprise can be justified on farms where it is a marginal choice on strict profit considerations as a way of ploughing back money into the farm business to limit income tax liabilities. Some farmers regard their beef cattle as a liquid capital 'store'.

The non-profit reasons for keeping beef cattle are emphasised much less nowadays than formerly which is right and proper given that profit margins are tight all round. But there is still a mistaken view that profitability depends more on skilful buying and selling than it does on sound planning and good management. Happily, growing numbers of farmers realise that, whilst buying and selling prices have an important bearing on average margins, consistent profitability depends on having a planned beef system operated at high standards of technical performance.

PRODUCTION SYSTEMS

In any country where forage growth is interrupted by cold winter weather or a dry season, production planning is dominated by the seasonal scarcity of forage. So, until fairly recently, cattle in temperate climates were expected to make gains cheaply from grazed grass during the summer, as many as possible were slaughtered for meat before the onset of winter and overwintered cattle were fed meagre rations and lost weight. Even allowing for compensatory growth at grass after a period of winter feed restriction, cattle did not reach slaughter condition until at least 30 months of age, often much older.

In the last 20 years or so improved techniques of forage conservation and the availability of relatively inexpensive cereal grains have transformed winter feeding. Severe winter store periods have been virtually eliminated and as a result lifetime daily gains have increased sharply. The net result has been a substantial reduction in average age at slaughter to less than two years of age. Also, slaughterings are spread more evenly through the year with a much smaller peak in the autumn.

These changes in feeding have led to a much greater range of beef systems, with an increase in winter finishing systems and the development of systems which produce beef throughout the year.

Nevertheless, the limited availability of winter feed and its cost still have a bearing on production decisions. Many suckled calf producers, for example, calve in the spring trading off the lighter weaning weight than from autumn-born calves against lower feed costs.

For the same reasons the tradition in suckler herds has been to sell calves at the autumn sales, sparing feed for the cows. As will be seen later, it is now possible to improve herd profitability by overwintering calves for sale as stores in the spring or by feeding them through to slaughter.

Many of the yearling suckled calves purchased by finishers at the autumn sales are fed for slaughter the following spring at 15–18 months of age. Lighter calves are overwintered and a high proportion of them are slaughtered off grass the following summer at 18–20 months old. The remainder are yarded, either for winter finishing, or for overwintering in preparation for grass finishing the next season at 27–30 months of age.

In the autumn and spring suckler-bred and dairy-bred cattle at intermediate stages of production are sold in large numbers at store markets. Some cattle may change hands two or even three times during their lifetime. It is this practice which has led to an excessive preoccupation with short-term feeding and the big effect on margins of buying and selling prices. It also results in cattle being reared on many farms without proper pre-planning. Cattle are purchased without clear production objectives and may be sold because prices seem good at the time or sale is enforced because feed supplies run out. Only by a systematic approach with clear-cut production

Table 5.1 Characteristics of planned dairy beef systems for Friesian/Holsteins.

	Cereal beef	Grass silage beef	18-month beef	Grass beef
Slaughter age (months)	11.5	16	18	22
Daily gain (kg)	1.3	1.0	0.85	0.8
Slaughter weight (kg)	460	500	500	550
Concentrates (tonnes)	1.8	1.0	1.0	0.5
Silage (tonnes 25% DM)	—	6.0	5.5	5.0
Stocking (cattle/ha)	—	8.5	3.5	2.5

and marketing targets can resource use be planned and exploited.

It is in beef production from dairy-bred calves that planned systems have made most progress. Several methods of production have been developed with planned inputs and production targets. A feature of these is that, except perhaps for calf rearing, the whole production cycle takes place on the same farm.

These planned systems vary in the amount of concentrates fed, the way in which grass is utilised and age and weight at slaughter (Table 5.1). At one extreme is cereal beef with housed cattle fed an all-concentrate diet through to slaughter at 11–13 months. At the other extreme is grass finishing at 20–24 months of age. Intermediate are the popular 18-month and grass silage beef systems, the latter being the first year-round production system based on grass.

Planned production does not imply inflexibility. There is scope to mould the system to individual farm circumstances and the plan can be adapted during production according to the progress made by cattle and the availability of feed. Inevitably there is some loss of flexibility, especially the opportunity to respond to short-term changes in cattle prices. In reality, when producers do attempt to take advantage of rising cattle prices they usually do it too late to cash in. Moreover, short-term decisions usually have longer-term consequences disrupting the flow of cattle and leaving feed unused. On most occasions it pays best to follow through the original plan.

Many beef enterprises are far too complicated with a wide range of purchase dates, cattle weights, sex and breed types. The complications are added to by continually re-grouping the cattle. It may be an approach which in theory spreads risks and keeps options open but it does so at the cost of a loss of control. There is a lot to be said for a single system using one type of cattle, or if the enterprise is large enough two systems which complement each other.

ENTERPRISE PLANNING

The ultimate objective of the beef enterprise is to contribute to net farm profit. So, not only must the selected beef system be potentially profitable in its own right, but it must match the resources available and be complementary to other enterprises on the farm.

Choosing a beef system

Choosing a beef system for the farm is best done with the help of an independent adviser who can make an objective assessment of available resources – land, buildings, capital – and can assess the standards of performance likely to be achieved with stockworker and managerial skills. Then realistic budgets can be drawn up and conclusions drawn on the best system for the farm. Money spent on planning at this stage will reap dividends later on.

Financial margins vary considerably from one beef system to another and from year to year. When budgeting it is advisable to look at margins over a number of years. The five-year gross margins for beef systems shown in Table 5.2, used together with targets presented in the production chapters provide a solid basis for budgeting and can be updated from published results. Beware of over-optimistic forecasts of cattle performance and stocking.

In general, the longer the production cycle the higher is the gross margin per head and the smaller are year-to-year fluctuations. Short-term finishing systems suffer worst from fluctuating margins, illustrated only too well by the ups and downs of winter finishing suckled calves.

It is interesting to observe how the relative profitability of beef systems changes over time. Through the 1970s 18-month beef produced the highest margins and many lowland suckler herds were dispersed to make way for 18-month beef units. Then with stagnant beef prices in the mid-1980s 18-month beef margins declined and now with ultra-high prices for dairy-bred calves and high interest rates many lowland farmers are reinstating suckler herds. Also, the grass silage beef system makes more intensive use of grassland and has supplanted 18-month beef on some farms.

There are occasions when a beef system with relatively low margins might be preferred for an individual farm. For example, grass finishing of dairy-bred calves has much lower working capital requirements than grass silage beef which might tip the balance of choice. Also, because only modest winter gains are required in the grass beef system, feeds need not be of finishing

Table 5.2 Average gross margins for the main beef systems. (Source: *MLC Beef Yearbook*, 1988.)

	1983	1984	1985	1986	1987	1988	Five-year average (Adjusted for inflation)
	Actual gross margin (£)						
Calf rearing							
– gross margin per head	19	21	21	25	27	–	25
Cereal beef							
– gross margin per head	79	72	80	62	75	–	81
Grass silage beef							
– gross margin per head	147	122	136	138	133	–	149
– gross margin per ha	910	817	983	1005	995	–	1043
18-month beef							
– gross margin per head	–	144	156	147	143	199	173
– gross margin per ha	–	491	549	545	533	765	628
Upland suckler herd							
– gross margin per head	196	217	216	230	254	–	242
– gross margin per ha	255	312	352	341	361	–	352
Winter finishing suckled calves							
– gross margin per head	–	46	37	49	57	98	62
Overwintering and grass finishing stores							
– gross margin per head	96	100	106	96	108	–	107
– gross margin per ha	307	326	345	351	439	–	379

Table 5.3 Components of variable costs, 1987–88.

	Cereal beef	Grass silage beef	18-month beef	Grass beef
	% of total variable costs			
Concentrates	88	70	60	45
Forage/other feeds	4	20	19	38
Other costs	8	10	21	17
Total	100	100	100	100

quality which brings arable by-products into the reckoning for feeding.

It is important to recognise that beef systems vary in their sensitivity to input costs. Table 5.3 shows that a change in concentrate price would have the biggest impact on cereal beef but that forage systems are more sensitive to changes in concentrate price than they are to changes in forage costs. So when prices are rising over-dependence on concentrates would be most damaging to profitability.

Physical resources

The availability and quality of land, labour and buildings are very important factors determining the beef system which best fits farm resources.

Grass-based systems are dependent on the area and quality of grassland which determine the number and type of cattle which can be kept. On arable farms there is the consideration of whether a grass break is advantageous in the arable rotation. Fencing and water determine which fields can be grazed.

The other feeds available on the farm also have an impact. If an objective is to utilise relatively low quality arable by-products such as straw this may limit the selected enterprise to a spring calving suckler herd or overwintering store cattle.

Labour and stockmanship skills are very important and must be considered in relation to the labour situation on the whole farm. Tractor drivers may be quite adequate for feeding finishing cattle but suckler herd management and calf rearing require good stockworkers or performance and profitability soon suffer.

Calf rearing is a major issue on many farms and an increasing proportion of dairy beef producers opt to purchase reared calves at three months of age from specialist rearers. They have to lay out more cash and forego the rearing margin but probably purchase calves reared to a higher standard than they could achieve themselves. Moreover, stock management is simplified and there can be a cash flow advantage if production involves overlapping batches of cattle.

Buildings also have an important bearing on the choice of beef system. If there are no buildings suitable for calf rearing this would reinforce a decision to purchase reared calves. For older cattle the type and layout of buildings dictate whether self-feeding of silage is possible, how long feeding takes, the scope for mechanised feeding and whether bull beef production is practicable. It is worth remembering that with year-round production of grass silage beef, the annual capacity of buildings is up to 20 per cent greater than when a single group is reared each year.

Associated with the buildings good cattle handling facilities are an often overlooked essential (see Chapter 6).

Financial planning

Budgeting may be used to examine the relationship between inputs and outputs, to study how a new or existing beef enterprise contributes to overall farm profit, or to look at the effects of changes in the balance between enterprises on the farm.

It is conventional to differentiate between *variable costs* of direct inputs such as feeds, seeds, fertilisers, veterinary services, marketing costs, etc., and *fixed costs* such as wages, machinery, rent, general overheads and interest charges on borrowed money which are 'common' to the farm establishment.

For many years the gross margin concept has been used (and misused) for farm planning. It is defined as the *output* of cattle sales less purchases of stock and losses due to mortality *minus variable costs.*

Gross margins are extremely useful for comparing management on farms where fixed costs differ, for analysing the financial consequences of different levels of technical performance, for fine-tuning an enterprise and for minor adjustment of the balance between enterprises.

Gross margins can be used in the early stages of planning to give an idea of the inputs and outputs. The trouble is that by ignoring fixed costs they can give a misleading impression of total costs. Silage is a classic example. The variable costs of silage making – seeds, fertiliser, silage additive, plastic sheeting, etc. – normally work out at about £5 per tonne, but by the time rent, machinery costs, labour and so on have been added the total cost is often nearer £20 per tonne. It is possible for apparently healthy gross margins to be associated with net losses if fixed costs are high.

Some farmers argue incorrectly that because of this deficiency the gross margin concept is outmoded. What they are really saying is that they do not know enough about the fixed costs profiles of their farms. Against a background of tight profit margins and growing fixed costs, farmers need to know more about the magnitude of fixed costs and how they are used by the mix of enterprises which make up the farm business. The problem is that there is no notional way of doing this because fixed costs vary so much from one farm to another, exceptionally by a factor of two.

Every farmer should study his accounts to work out the general level of fixed costs and if possible allocate them between enterprises. At the very least it is important to know what fixed costs would or could be eliminated if an enterprise was discontinued.

The deduction from output of variable costs and fixed costs which can be assigned to the enterprise leaves a value called the net margin which is different from, but easily confused with, net profit. Despite this possible confusion the net margin is extremely useful in focusing attention on those fixed costs which could be eliminated or would have to be transferred to other enterprises if beef production stopped.

Having focused attention on fixed costs it is important to question whether they are too high for the type of farm. Are there too many tractors? Are machinery repairs too costly because of careless use or lack of regular maintenance? Could more machinery and building repairs be carried out by farm staff? Would it be cheaper to use a contractor for specialist jobs? Is the labour force right for the farm? What could be done to reduce bank borrowings? And so on ...

High interest rates on borrowed money also require that a close watch is kept on the working capital invested in beef production and how that enterprise contributes to the cash flow of the whole farm. The usual convention is to calculate average working capital as the cost of the purchased animal plus half the variable costs. The interest charge can then be worked out using current rates which are frequently two per cent above the bank rate.

Working capital requirements depend both on the duration of the beef system and its seasonality. The longer the production cycle, the greater is the working capital requirement and the higher its peak value. Seasonal factors are also important, for example in 18-month beef where a second batch of calves must be purchased before cattle from the first batch are sold for slaughter. This causes much more fluctuation in working capital requirements during the year than for, say, a suckler herd where the initial capital investment in cows is high but thereafter working capital fluctuates within a narrow range.

Table 5.4 Gross margin budget worksheet for grass silage beef.

Numbers reconciliation	Cattle valuation (£)		
No. of cattle at start	Closing valuation		
+ Calf purchases	– Opening valuation		
– Cattle sales	= Change in valuation ±		£ _____

Gross margin budget (£)

Output

Cattle sales	cattle	kg	@ £/kg	
– Calf purchases	calves @ £			
± Change in valuation				
			Output	£ _____

Variable costs

Milk replacer	t @	£/t		
Concentrates:				
early weaning	t @	£/t	£	
protein supplement	t @	£/t	£	
cereal	t @	£/t	£	
			Total concentrates	
Other feeds:				
	t @	£/t	£	
	t @	£/t	£	
	t @	£/t	£	
			Total other feed	
Forage:				
reseeding seeds £	+ sprays £		£	
fertiliser	t @	£/t	£	
	t @	£/t	£	
	t @	£/t	£	
silage additive	t @	£/t	£	
silage sheeting			£	
			Total forage	
Veterinary:				
veterinary services			£	
medicines			£	
growth promoters			£	
			Total veterinary	
Bedding	t @	£/t		
Other costs:				
cattle transport			£	
advisory services			£	
miscellaneous			£	
			Total other costs	_____
			Total variable costs	£ _____
			Gross margin	£ _____

The working capital profile has inevitable effects on cash flow which measures the difference between receipts and expenditure month by month. The cash flow of the beef enterprise may dictate purchasing and marketing policies for other enterprises or it may create or aggravate a shortage of working capital.

Cash flow problems are inevitably greatest in beef systems with seasonal sales. Level cash flow is an attraction of year-round production systems such as cereal beef and grass silage beef. On larger farms there may be an opportunity to dovetail two systems whose peak working capital requirements occur at different times to even out the cash flow.

For an established beef enterprise it is necessary to draw up a budget each year setting tough but realistic standards of technical performance and forecasting costs and returns. Given an awareness of fixed costs the gross margin format will do perfectly well and an example worksheet for grass silage beef is shown in Table 5.4. This annual budget gives an indication of profit potential and provides a reference for any adjustments to the plan which prove necessary because performance departs from the standards set, feed supplies are not as expected or prices are different from forecasts.

Periodically it is worth examining the consequences of altering the balance between the beef enterprise and competing enterprises. This is best done using the technique of partial budgeting in which a list is drawn up of all changes in income and expenditure due to alterations in size of alternative enterprises. The analysis gives important information about replanning at the margin between enterprises and may raise important questions about performance standards and cost structures which warrant more detailed analysis at the whole enterprise level.

Records of performance

The very mention of recording is enough to make most farmers shuffle their feet and try to switch the conversation to another subject. The reality is that records are such an important aid to profitable management that no serious beef producer can afford to be without them.

Simple records are all that is needed to pin-point strengths and weaknesses of the beef enterprise and to spot any drift away from peformance targets while there is still time to put matters right. The key information includes details of cattle purchases and sales, calving records for suckler cows, daily gains, veterinary treatments, amounts of silage and concentrates fed, fertiliser applications and the grassland area devoted to the beef enterprise. The information must be written down because memory is not the basis of a sound recording system.

Every beef producer should have a good quality weighcrush installed in a well-designed handling system. Cattle in housed beef systems should be weighed at about three-monthly intervals and grazing cattle at turnout and yarding. To speed up weighing and the interpretation of results cattle should be fitted with easily-read ear tags and the numbers listed in order on the weighing record sheet so that they can be found quickly. Then any animal with poor gains between weighings is spotted straight away while it is still in the crush.

Only through regular weighings can rations be set and adjusted and daily gains checked against production targets. More frequent weighing during the final stages of finishing, at about monthly intervals, is a great help in managing cattle marketing.

It is easy enough to devise a DIY recording system but various organisations offer professionally designed services with an advisory back-up. The advantage of using an independent adviser is that it disciplines record keeping, interpretation of the results and taking appropriate action to keep performance on target. The costs can be recouped many times over.

6 Buildings and Equipment

Investment in buildings and equipment must be considered with care because, as seen in the previous chapter, it is all too easy for fixed costs to escalate to a point where net profit evaporates. The first step, therefore, before committing expenditure is to work out the annual charge for depreciation and interest payments and to set these against budgeted profits.

BUILDINGS

Building costs

The capital cost of a new building needs to be paid off over the period of its estimated useful life. Obsolescence usually affects usefulness sooner than deterioration of the building structure itself. So a specialist calf house should probably be depreciated over 10 years, other cattle buildings over 15 years and a general purpose building which could be adapted for other uses over 20 years.

The calculation of annual charges includes both depreciation of the capital sum and bank interest on the capital outstanding each year (amortisation). The crude way of doing the calculation is to assume repayment of the capital in equal instalments over the write-off period and to calculate interest on half the capital sum. The annual figure calculated this way is slightly below the real annual cost but is good enough for practical budgeting.

Example:
The annual charge per £1000 borrowed at 15 per cent over 10 years is

$$\frac{1000}{10} + (500 \times 0.15) = £175$$

In addition to the annual charge any other costs associated with the new building should be taken into account, such as fuel and power, insurance, building maintenance, etc. The other side of the coin is that the building may bring benefits of easier management, more efficient labour use and improved cattle performance which can be set against costs.

Investment is straightforward if profits are sufficient to pay off the capital sum and give a return on the investment. The more usual situation is where margins are hardly sufficient to justify the investment. It may still be possible to justify the building on other grounds. The beef enterprise may strengthen the farm business by spreading risks or by introducing a grass break bringing higher arable crop yields. The FYM may reduce expenditure on granular fertilisers.

One of the most important factors deciding whether to put up a new building and when is inflation. Because of inflation the cheapest time to erect a building is now. Even when present profits cannot finance annual charges, once the building is erected its cost is fixed (except for interest charges) but other costs and returns are likely to rise. There are many cases where buildings were erected against professional advice which only a few years later seem a sound investment. Nevertheless the proper justification for an investment is an evaluation based on present profits.

One way of making a doubtful building project viable is to reduce costs by doing part of the work using farm staff. Many farmers are quite capable of taking on excavation work, concreting and blockwork at much lower cost than the contractor. Concreting in particular is worth doing because it accounts for a high proportion of total building costs and is a skill soon learned. The jobs can make good use of farm labour in a slack season.

The *Farm Building Cost Guide* published by the Centre for Rural Building, Craibstone, Aberdeen, gives useful guidelines on costs for various types of building.

Building design

Building design affects cattle performance and ventilation is particularly important. Design needs to take account of the size of feeding groups, the bedding system, whether bull beef is produced, feeding and watering arrangements and the efficiency and safety of stockworkers.

Flexibility of use is advantageous provided it is not achieved at the cost of current inefficiency. As an example, it is wise to make feeding passages wide enough to take a forage box even if this method of feeding is not contemplated at present.

Group size and space allowances

Group size has an important bearing on the internal design of a building.

Table 6.1 Space allowances for housed cattle (sq metres).

Liveweight (kg)	Straw bedding	Slatted floors
50–250	1.0–2.0	Not suitable
250–450	2.0–3.0	1.5–2.0
450–600	3.0–4.5	2.0–2.5
Suckler cows	5.0–6.0	3.0–3.5

Small groups of cattle are easier to manage and probably perform better and with less variability. Breed types and sexes with different performance characteristics can be penned separately and rationed accurately. In general, 40 should be considered the upper limit for groups of steers and heifers. The safety code for bull beef proposes a limit of 20 in a group. Of course, the smaller the pen size the greater is the cost for pen divisions, gates and water supply.

Precise space allowances depend on the layout of pens within the building but Table 6.1 gives general guidelines for straw bedding and slatted floors. With slatted floors it is important to keep stocking rates high so that the slats self-clean, otherwise there is a build-up of dung.

Floors

Straw bedding is the choice wherever straw is available. In a winter of six months, cattle of 300–500 kg need about a tonne of straw per head and produce double that quantity of FYM. Requirements are greater when silage is fed because of the looseness of the dung and high rates of urine production. The approach should always be to use sufficient bedding to keep the cattle clean which contributes to better hygiene at the meat plant and reduces the cost of tanning hides in leather production.

Cereal beef cattle, where consumption of a small quantity of straw lessens the risk of bloat, should be bedded daily. With other cattle the chore of bedding can usually be reduced to every other day. Making sure that straw in the field is dry before baling so that there is no moulding in the stack, and careful handling during bedding, help to keep down dust levels and reduce the incidence of pneumonia.

Some saving of straw can be made by leaving an unbedded concrete strip behind the feed barrier which is scraped clean at least three times a week. This also avoids the need for feed and water troughs to be raised as bedding builds up if the whole area is bedded.

In marginal land areas far from arable farms straw is expensive and consideration must be given to cubicles or slatted floors.

Cubicles are widely and successfully used in dairy cattle buildings but have limitations in beef production. Male cattle urinate onto the centre of the cubicle which can create drainage problems. These can be overcome by concreting the cubicle floor and overlaying it with one of the synthetic cow beds with a springy texture which gives extra comfort. Cubicles are not really suitable for bulls because their riding behaviour risks damage to bulls and cubicles alike.

Spring calving beef cows, which are pregnant through the winter, are perfectly at home in a cubicle house but for autumn calvers there is the problem of arranging lying areas and creeps for the calves. During natural mating problems occur with false services of cows not in heat, the bull may damage himself or the cubicles may be damaged.

The choice of slatted floors includes welfare considerations as well as building cost and labour efficiency. Without doubt cattle suffer more problems on slatted floors than on straw bedding. There is a higher incidence of foot and leg injuries and tail injuries caused by trampling which in the summer months can become infected, in extreme cases leading to complete loss of the tail.

These problems are much greater with extra-active Friesian/Holstein bulls than with steers or quieter beef breed × Friesians and suckler-bred cattle. For similar reasons there are problems in mating suckler cows on slatted floors which cannot be overcome satisfactorily. Indeed, the British welfare code recommends that cows should not be kept on totally slatted floors and prefers bedding for all classes of cattle.

Clearly slat performance is influenced by slat design, including gap width, and the materials specification. However, it is not clear what is the ideal specification and work is in progress on coatings which make slats more comfortable. The current preference is for flat concrete slats 125 mm wide at the top, tapering to a narrower width at the bottom, and with a 30–40 mm gap between slats. The slats are laid parallel to the feed barrier.

Whether buildings are constructed with high level slats, with dung handled underneath as a semi-solid, or low level slats with dung handled as a liquid or scraped as a slurry, depends on the aspect of the building and the compromise between the greater costs of high level slats but the greater convenience of less frequent emptying.

High stocking densities in slatted buildings reduce air volume around and over the cattle and special attention must therefore be paid to ventilation.

The best advice to anyone contemplating slatted floors is to lean on the experiences of neighbours in building design, choice of slats and management of cattle on them. In isolated areas where straw is too expensive to use as bedding, slats have a place for growing cattle and winter housing dry suckler cows. But elsewhere their use will probably decline.

Ventilation

Whatever the choice of flooring in the building, good ventilation is essential to minimise the incidence of pneumonia which causes so much morbidity and mortality. The objective is an airy, dry atmosphere without draughts or dust – stale, humid air laden with dust from careless handling of bedding straw is a recipe for enzootic pneumonia. Low temperature is not a problem for cattle in the British climate because ruminants have spare heat to dissipate. Buildings which seem exposed by human standards are much healthier for cattle than those with a stuffy atmosphere.

In a conventional ⌂–pitched-roof building the usual method of letting air in is through 'space boarding' in the upper side walls where vertical wooden slats are fixed with gaps between them. This allows air to pass into the building freely but cuts out draughts. In addition the building needs an 'exhaust' to get rid of stale air. The best way of achieving this is to have a continuously open ridge. With warm air rising from around the cattle the combination of space boarding and an open ridge creates a free flow of fresh air through the building.

There is a lot to be said for open-fronted monopitch buildings with a ⌐ profile. Space boarding in the rear wall gives a free flow of air. The roof projects beyond the front of the pen to give some weather protection. In wintry weather these buildings seem very exposed but cattle do well in them.

Wide buildings are especially difficult to ventilate because the natural circulation of air is poor. Also if buildings are clustered close together, swirling air currents can cause problems. Required ventilation rates rise dramatically in hot summer weather and where cattle are housed year-round it helps if whole sections of space boarding can be removed to increase air flow. Even so it may prove necessary to reduce stocking densities in summer.

Feeding

The types of feed and the system of feeding affect the type of feed barrier and feeding space per animal which in turn predetermine pen dimensions.

For cattle fed concentrates *ad lib.* the feed hopper can be placed anywhere in the pen where it can be serviced conveniently. The cattle need a trough space allowance at the feed hopper of at least 75 mm per head, preferably 100 mm. Where silage is self-fed from a clamp the minimum space allowance is 175 mm per head.

The commonest situation is where concentrates are rationed with silage fed to appetite; the concentrate allowance is sprinkled on top of the silage once or twice daily. For this feeding method all the cattle need to be able to feed at once with the following minimum space allowances:

Liveweight (kg)	Space at feed barrier (mm)
Up to 250	400
250–450	500
450+	600
Suckler cows	750

Using these values a pen for 40 steers or heifers fed rationed concentrates would require 500 mm per head at the feed barrier and a floor space of 3 square metres. The pen would have dimensions of 20 metres wide by 6 metres deep. With a scraped concrete feeding passage within the pen this leaves a rather shallow bedded area unless the overall floor space allowance is increased. On a similar diet fed to bulls in a slatted floor building, a pen for 20 bulls with a floor space allowance of 2 square metres would have dimensions of 10 metres wide by 4 metres deep.

The problems of providing sufficient trough space for feeding rationed concentrates in pens with sensible overall dimensions has led to the installation of devices such as lateral troughs running the depth of the pen. Certainly these provide additional trough space but they are awkward, at times dangerous, to service because the stockworker has to stand in the trough to feed cattle as they jostle to get at the feed.

The other approach is to use a 'complete' feed in which the concentrates and forage are thoroughly mixed. In many units using complete rations only two thirds of the cattle can feed at once. In theory this is fine but in practice cattle prefer the feed when it is fresh so there is a good deal of competition to feed first. The effect of this can be lessened by feeding twice or even three times daily, which is the practice in many USA feedlots.

Big bale silage is usually fed in a 'ring feeder' which is a circular structure 1250–1800 mm in diameter. The structure includes vertical or diagonal feeding rails and with the bottom section covered with solid metal sheeting to limit waste. The big bale is placed in the feeder and the cattle are left to get on with it. These feeders are cheap but silage wastage can be 10–15 per cent.

Water

An unlimited supply of clean drinking water is essential. Water troughs are best because they allow several cattle to drink at once. However, it is difficult to prevent troughs being fouled. In many modern buildings water bowls are preferred. There needs to be a water bowl to every 20 cattle. Guard rails are needed to prevent rubbing, plastic water piping needs to be guarded against chewing and the whole system should be protected against frost.

Provision must be made to raise troughs and water bowls as bedding builds up but it is easier if the water supply is placed in a non-bedded section of the pen. The tendency is to locate the water supply out of the way at the rear of the pen but inspection and maintenance are easier if location is at the front.

Bull beef

The secure housing and safe management of bulls requires special provision in building design. As already mentioned, group size should not exceed 20 bulls. As far as possible buildings should be designed so that stockworkers can service the pens without having to enter them. If a stockworker does have to enter a pen he should carry a stick and a second stockworker should be posted outside the pen as a lookout.

The British safety code for bull beef production recommends that pen divisions and gates should have childproof vertical bars or that the bull beef unit should have a secure perimeter fence. All pen divisions and gates should be 1.5 metres high with secure catches on gates. The buildings should be well-lit to allow easy inspection at night. Warning signs should be erected on buildings with a bull's head within a yellow triangle with a black surround.

Calf housing

The infant calf has special environmental requirements, particularly if it has been purchased from another farm, and is stressed and susceptible to disease. During the milk feeding period the calf is more susceptible to low temperatures than older ruminating cattle. Under British conditions winter temperatures are rarely low enough to cause problems, provided buildings are draught-free. Nevertheless it is useful to have heating lamps available for newly delivered or sick calves.

The trend in calf building design is away from environment-controlled buildings to naturally ventilated structures which provide airy but draught-free conditions and a dry bed. A simple open-fronted monopitch building with space boarding in the rear wall to assist ventilation and at least 6 cubic metres of air space per calf can give excellent results.

Within the building milk-fed calves are best penned singly in solid sided pens with minimum dimensions of 1.8 × 1.0 metres mounted on concrete floors with a 1 in 20 fall to the drainage system. In cold winter weather it is advisable to erect a kennel structure over the rear half of the pens using straw bales or timber panels. In a monopitch building with solid walls between bays, i.e. a loose-box structure, a bay holding 14–16 single pens either side of a central feeding passage gives ideal overall dimensions.

At weaning an option in a pen like this is simply to dismantle the individual pens, bed the whole floor area and leave the calves where they are. This avoids the stress of moving calves to separate follow-on accommodation. There is sufficient space to house the calves right through to six months of age if necessary.

The same building design is also suitable for the group housing of calves for *ad libitum* milk feeding. Again, in winter it is advisable to erect a kennel structure in which the calves can snuggle to find warmth.

CATTLE HANDLING

Every beef unit, however small, needs good cattle handling/loading facilities, otherwise handling is time-consuming and puts stockworkers and cattle at risk. Provided care is taken over design the handling set-up can be erected at very reasonable cost using second-hand materials and farm labour with the main expenditure reserved for a top-of-the-range weigh-crush.

The basic elements are a collecting pen incorporating a chute leading into a race at the end of which is located the weigh-crush and one or more dispersal pens from which cattle can be loaded onto cattle lorries. Ideally there should be two dispersal pens with a shedding gate at the crush so that groups of cattle can be subdivided. Fences and gates should be at least 1.6 m high.

The collecting pen/chute should provide 1.7 square metres of space for finishing cattle and 2.5 square metres for a suckler cow and her calf. Circular collecting pens are the easiest to control and cattle move best along curving races where they do not see the crush until the last moment. In practice, rectangular designs are the easiest to construct and work well provided the design rules are followed.

The collecting pen should have a gate between the pen itself and the chute so that cattle can be forced into the head of the race. The angle on the slanting fence of the chute should be 30° to the line of the race so that cattle do not jam in the mouth of the race. In the race itself, which should be at least 8 metres long, there should be provision for inserting tail bars to stop cattle backing-up.

Dispersal pens should be larger than collecting pens so that cattle can calm down after handling. Allow 2.5 square metres for finishing cattle and 3.5 square metres for a suckler cow and calf. In locating and designing the dispersal pen remember to allow for vehicle access unless separate loading facilities are provided.

EQUIPMENT

The importance of controlling fixed costs has been stressed several times and this requires careful justification of machinery and equipment costs. The smaller the farm the more important this is.

On the arable farm tractors, fertiliser spreaders etc. are shared with crop enterprises but there is always the temptation to keep an extra tractor, albeit an old one, so that a piece of equipment can be left mounted ready for use instead of having to swop over. It may be convenient but it costs money.

Silage-making equipment is expensive and before committing expenditure it is worth checking the cost of local contractors and their availability precisely when required. Contractors may be used to muck out buildings. The same argument must be applied to home milling and mixing – is it that much cheaper to do the job on the farm or should the work be contracted out to a neighbour or local feed mill?

When silage is the main feed its sheer bulk demands an efficient feeding system. The trend is away from tower silos and automated feeding systems because of the high cost, lack of flexibility and breakdowns. There is also a trend away from simple self-feeding systems in favour of trough feeding with higher targets of cattle performance.

Silage is usually removed from the clamp using a hydraulic fork or block cutter; the block cutter leaves a tidy silage face and so minimises undesirable secondary fermentation, especially in warm summer weather. Then silage is delivered to the cattle using a front loader or a forage box, possibly with the concentrate allowance mixed with the silage. It is difficult to justify the cost of a forage box for small numbers of cattle but for larger groups or where cattle are housed in various buildings scattered around the farmstead it certainly takes the chore out of feeding and releases the stockworker for his proper function – which is managing the cattle.

7 Grassland Management

During the last decade specialists have done a fine job unravelling the complexities of grassland management and presenting their conclusions as four simple rules of good management:

(1) Use sward height to control the management of grazing cattle.
(2) Use a reserve (buffer) grazing area to make good temporary shortages of grass.
(3) In the integration of grazing and cutting management, give priority to grazing.
(4) Cut early and frequently for high quality silage.

The application of these four practical rules offers the hope of an acceleration in the rate of improvement of grassland management to add to the transformation which has occurred already since the Second World War. In that time output per hectare of grassland has roughly doubled.

Nevertheless, on many farms grassland management is still the weak link. It is not so much that insufficient N fertiliser is applied to grow grass, but

Table 7.1 Grassland management in commercial beef production. (Source: *MLC Beef Yearbook*, 1988.)

	Bottom third	Average	Top third
Grass silage beef			
N fertiliser (kg N/ha)	300	325	375
Stocking (cattle/ha)	5.6	7.5	8.9
Liveweight gain (kg/ha)	2034	2820	3506
18-month beef			
N fertiliser (kg N/ha)	220	227	230
Stocking (cattle/ha)	3.2	3.9	4.2
Liveweight gain (kg/ha)	1298	1629	1859
Spring calving lowland suckler herds			
N fertiliser (kg N/ha)	120	134	145
Stocking (cows/ha)	2.0	2.1	2.5
Calf gain (kg/ha)	400	451	579

rather that the stocking rate adopted is not high enough to exploit the grass grown. Just what can be achieved is shown by commercial producers recorded by MLC who achieved the top third of gross margins per hectare (Table 7.1).

GROWING GRASS

Each tiller (shoot) of a grass plant produces a succession of new leaves from a growing point near its base, well out of harm's way when swards are cut or grazed at a normal severity of defoliation. Moreover, because the new leaf is enclosed in a sheath provided by older leaves it is protected to some extent against treading. The leaves grow and after a life span of about four weeks die. The ultimate objective of each tiller overwintered from the previous

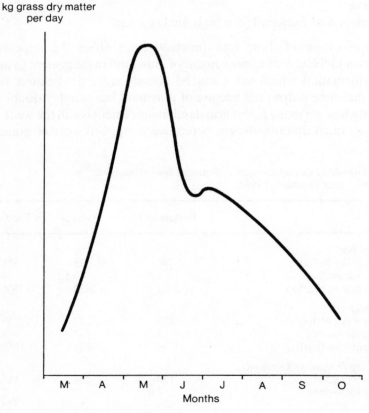

Fig. 7.1 Seasonal pattern of grass growth.

season is to flower and produce seed. Grassland management for beef production seeks to prevent this by grazing and cutting to keep the sward in a leafy state and encourage the production of highly digestible vegetative tillers.

Grass growth is at its peak in May and then declines through the dry mid-summer period until July when late summer rain causes a slight increase in production followed by a steady decline through the autumn (Figure 7.1).

The potential for grass production depends on the inherent quality of the site as indicated by soil type, latitude, altitude, drainage and summer rainfall. And then the actual level of production is governed by sward type, fertiliser application and the grassland management policy.

There are two contrasting approaches to forage production. Most common is grass swards receiving applications of N fertiliser to increase grass growth. The alternative is to use grass/clover swards which fix their own N from the atmosphere and produce herbage yields equivalent to grass fertilised with 150–200 kg N per hectare. This is the approach which has been used so successfully in New Zealand.

Heavily fertilised grass swards out-yield grass/clover swards but this is only part of the story and financial analysis (see Chapter 10) shows that there is a place for grass/clover. Moreover, in a period of concern about environmental matters and production surpluses a more extensive approach to grassland management is emotionally and politically attractive.

The response to N fertiliser is virtually linear up to 200–300 kg N per hectare at 15–30 kg grass dry matter per kg N, depending on site quality and previous management. Beyond that there is a diminishing response curve, especially on poorer quality sites, and practical maximum levels for beef production range from 250 kg N on poor sites to 450 kg N on the best sites. But note that recommended levels of N fertiliser may be lower than these for some beef systems.

Responses to N fertiliser have been recorded by cut yields in grassland manuring trials. Under grazing conditions there is a recycling of N via dung and urine and soil N builds up in established leys. These effects can partly obscure the effects of site quality at medium levels of N fertiliser application and could explain why MLC results from farms fail to demonstrate expected differences between sites of apparently different quality. What differences do appear are most likely to occur from mid-season onwards.

The timing of the spring N fertiliser application is as important as the total quantity. Applications should begin just before grass growth starts. The best known rule of thumb for deciding the date of first application is the T-sum technique which originated in Holland. This is calculated, starting at 1 January, by adding up the mean daily temperatures in °C (counting minus values as zero) until they total 200. In most years this means applying the first N fertiliser as soon as ground conditions permit in February in south west England and early coastal zones and in March elsewhere.

For first-cut silage the first application should be about 125 kg N per hectare with 100 kg for the second cut and 80 kg for later cuts applied as soon as the previous cut has been cleared. Some farmers split the first application to cut down the risk of leaching in a wet spring.

Grazing areas need N fertiliser little and often and a useful guideline is $2\frac{1}{2}$ kg N per hectare per day. So a rotationally grazed paddock due to be grazed again in three weeks should receive about 50 kg N per hectare. Continuously-grazed swards can be fertilised with the cattle present, dressing about a third of the area every 10 days with 75 kg N per hectare. It is not worth applying N fertiliser after the end of August because there is usually more than enough soil N to support autumn growth.

On farms where grazing is the predominant activity it is beneficial to reduce the early and late season N applications slightly but to increase the applications in May and June. This has no effect on total yield but evens out production, giving a useful increase in mid-season even under dry conditions.

It must be remembered that N fertiliser increases soil acidity in direct proportion to the amount applied. So as soon as soil pH falls below 5.5 lime should be applied to restore it to 6.0 – 6.5.

Regular soil sampling is necessary not only to check pH but also to monitor potassium and phosphorus status so that potash (K_2O) and phosphate (P_2O_5) fertilisers can be supplied to support high levels of grass or grass/clover production. Slurry is a useful source of potash for conservation areas.

Conservation removes substantial quantities of potassium which is replaced by applying 0.5 kg K_2O per hectare for each kg N applied. In a three-cut silage regime this would be achieved by applying 160 kg K_2O per hectare. This is best done in mid-season using a compound fertiliser also containing N for the next silage cut. If suckler cows are grazing it is best to avoid spring application because this increases the risk of hypomagnesaemic tetany.

On grazed swards there may be no need for potash on clay soils but a high requirement up to 60 kg K_2O per hectare on poor light soils.

Phosphate requirements for grazed swards are usually met by applying 20–40 units P_2O_5 per hectare in mid-season using a compound fertiliser also including N and K_2O. Conservation areas need about double this amount.

Sward composition has important effects on herbage yield, heading dates for silage making and the persistence of grassland. Perennial ryegrasses are unrivalled for all-round ability and are the cornerstone of most seeds mixtures. They are outyielded by Italian ryegrasses such as RvP but are much more persistent. Timothy, useful in mid-season but not competitive with ryegrass, and lower yielding cocksfoot and meadow fescue have been reduced to a minor role. Many seeds mixtures contain white clover which contributes to herbage production even when 200 kg N fertiliser per hectare is applied.

It is all too easy to become preoccupied with seeds mixtures and to forget that well-managed long leys and permanent pastures can have excellent botanical composition and rival the output of sown leys. Grassland should not be ploughed up and re-seeded expensively for the sake of it.

GRAZING MANAGEMENT

Grazing should be given priority where grazing and conservation are integrated because liveweight gains are made relatively cheaply from grazed grass and any loss of grazing performance must be recouped later on more expensive winter feed. In an unfavourable season this policy may result in a shortage of silage. However, there is considerable scope to redesign winter rations which allow production and marketing targets to be met without undermining profitability.

Grazing management should aim to control the surface height of the sward. This concept has made a fundamental contribution to the understanding of grazing management.

At low sward heights herbage intake falls because cattle are unable to put in sufficient extra work to maintain intake. Below a sward height of 3 cm grass production falls because there is insufficient leaf to sustain maximum grass growth. At high sward heights cattle graze selectively, leaving patches in the sward which run to seed. Later on, as grass production falls, cattle are forced to graze this low quality herbage and daily gain falls. So, controlling sward height not only controls grazing behaviour but also benefits pasture regrowth. It must be remembered that even with good control of sward height a relatively small proportion of the grass grown is consumed by the cattle.

The great advantage of using sward height as a management tool is that it can be used to control grazing day-by-day. For the first half of the grazing season sward height should be controlled at 6–8 cm on continuously grazed pastures, the upper end of that range for suckler cows and calves and the lower end for growing cattle. After mid-season when the risk of seed heading has lessened, sward heights of 8–10 cm can be allowed. On rotationally grazed paddocks cattle should be moved on when sward height falls to 8 cm early in the season, 10 cm later on. Ideally swards should be grazed down at the end of the season to a short 3–4 cm stubble which minimises winter kill. Sheep are ideal for this job.

Sward height can be measured with a rule or with one of the commercial 'sward sticks'; from the ground to the tips of the leaves is the sward height. A cruder method is the 'wellie test' which assumes that the upper surface of the foot of a Wellington boot is 6–8 cm above ground level. To get a clear idea of sward height several random measurements from grazed and ungrazed areas should be made walking a W-shaped route across the field.

There are two points to make about recommended sward heights. First, the grass is much shorter than conventional thinking considers appropriate for cattle. And second, sward control at recommended heights does imply very high stocking rates, especially early in the season when grass growth is at its peak. On grassland fertilised with 250 kg N per hectare the weight of cattle stocked at turnout needs to be at least 2.5 tonnes per hectare, which is 14 autumn-born Hereford × Friesian calves with a typical turnout weight of 180 kg.

Many farmers would be nervous about stocking so heavily because of the risk of running out of grass. This is a distinct possibility and so some method of buffering is necessary. One way is to feed concentrates if sward height falls too low. Another is the 'put-and-take' method of adjusting cattle numbers according to grass availability. Far better is the provision of a buffer grazing area. This is a reserve area adding between a quarter and a third to the minimum grazing area. Commonly it is part of one of the grazing fields split off by an electric fence.

The objective is to cut the buffer area for silage if possible. However, if sward height on the main grazing area falls to 5 cm then about a third of the buffer is opened up for grazing, allowing sward height on the main area to recover. If sward height on the main area still fails to recover then a further third of the buffer is grazed. In a poor season the whole of the buffer may be required for grazing. But in a good season the buffer can be cut for silage with the fresh aftermaths available for grazing later in the season. The situation could even arise where sward heights on the grazing areas increase above recommended levels in which case the buffer fence would be moved back into the grazing area.

In combination, the control of sward height and use of a grazing buffer give the confidence to adopt high grazing stocking rates. Target weights of cattle stocked are shown in Table 7.2 which at 250 kg N per hectare give a seasonal average of 2 tonnes of liveweight stocked. At target levels of daily gain of 0.8–0.9 kg per day this would produce a grazing gain of 1 tonne per hectare.

Table 7.2 Target stocking rates on grassland fertilised with 250 kg N per hectare.

	Liveweight stocked (tonnes/ha)
May	2.5
June	2.3
July	2.0
August	1.8
September	1.7
October	1.6
Grazing season	*2.0*

This analysis of grazing management has ignored grazing system though with a hint that continuous and rotational grazing are alternatives.

At one time rotational paddock grazing was considered an essential part of intensive grassland management. There was a preoccupation with paddock grazing layouts, some of which were complex with high fencing and watering costs. Subsequently it was realised that the apparent superiority of rotational grazing was due largely to the built-in discipline which led to efficient defoliation and high stocking rates. Now it has been established that continuous grazing with the same N fertiliser and stocking rate rivals the performance of rotational grazing. In consequence most producers have reverted to continuous grazing.

There are situations where rotational grazing still has a place. For example, though much needs to be learned about the management of clover swards, it seems likely that clover content would be maintained best in a paddock grazing system with rests between defoliations. Also, where there are two age groups of cattle on the farm – e.g. grass beef, rearing heifer replacements – there are benefits in grazing the younger age group ahead of the older cattle in a paddock system.

This leader/follower system of grazing uses about six paddocks and achieves high performance in the young cattle because they can graze selectively high up in the sward well out of the way of the main concentration of parasitic worm larvae in the base of the sward. The older cattle following behind perform well on the remaining grass and are more resistant to worms. All decisions on cattle management are made on the basis of sward height in the followers' paddock.

The system works well as long as the total appetite of the following group is greater than that of the leaders. In grass finishing a point is reached eventually where this is no longer the case because so many of the followers have been marketed. At this point the leaders would normally be moved to fresh aftermaths on previously conserved areas and leader/follower grazing discontinued.

The most extreme situation is where cattle are not grazed at all but cut grass is carried to them. This so-called zero grazing or green soiling is still quite common on dairy farms in parts of continental Europe. From time to time a mechanised approach has been tried in Britain, seeking to increase grassland output by eliminating fouling and trampling of the grass. But mechanisation costs are high and day-in, day-out it is difficult to provide cattle with a constant supply of high quality grass. Zero grazing has been largely supplanted by grass silage beef in which all the grass grown is made into silage which is fed to housed cattle (see Chapter 10).

PARASITIC WORM CONTROL

Cattle performance can be severely depressed by parasitic nematode roundworms which infect the alimentary system, causing parasitic gastro-enteritis. The abomasal *Ostertagia* spp cause the most serious losses in cattle. Young cattle during their first grazing season are most at risk. As cattle grow older they develop a resistance to worms but older cattle still deposit worm eggs on pasture via the faeces which develop into infective larvae.

One source of infection is worm eggs deposited during the previous grazing season, a few of which survive over winter. Danger from this source develops from March but on ungrazed swards has receded by the end of May. Another source of infection is from eggs deposited by older cattle grazing the same swards as susceptible calves; these develop into infective larvae and are a danger from May onwards. Most important of all is a small dose of infective larvae picked up by calves in the spring which generate heavy pasture levels of infective larvae from July onwards that re-infect the calves and depress growth performance. To be effective worm control needs to be an integral part of grassland management, including planned grassland use and the strategic use of anthelmintics to avert clinical symptoms and/or to limit pasture contamination with worm eggs.

It is important to observe several simple rules. Older cattle should not be allowed to graze 'clean' leys set aside for calves even for a few hours. Calves should be turned onto clean leys straight away and not via a convenient paddock near the buildings which is used year after year and perpetuates infection. If possible fields grazed by susceptible cattle one year should be conserved the next year and not grazed until July.

Where sheep and cattle are both kept there is the possibility of operating a clean grazing system using a three-year rotation of cattle, sheep, conservation. Even if this is not possible it is certainly worth alternating cattle and sheep.

Inevitably there are situations where young dairy-bred cattle are grazed on the same field for several years and strategic dosing with anthelmintics is necessary for worm control. There are three approaches to worm control. The first is a preventative strategy which seeks, not only to control worms, but also to limit the level of infective larvae on pasture. This is done by use of a drench, injection or pour-on product at intervals of about five weeks early in the season or by inserting a slow release bolus or pulse release bolus (with periodic releases of anthelmintic) at turnout. The second approach, which has worked well in the 18-month system, is to dose cattle once in mid-July and move them to fresh aftermath grazing. And thirdly, where a move to aftermath grazing is not possible, infection is suppressed by periodic dosing from mid-season or inserting an anthelmintic bolus.

On yarding cattle which are to be grazed again next season it is probably worth dosing to kill inhibited larvae; this prevents them from depositing worm eggs the following spring.

Husk caused by the lungworm *Dictyocaulus viviparus* is a killer on some farms. Most husk larvae die over winter but those that survive and eggs from cattle which grazed the previous season produce infective larvae which pose a threat during warm wet summer weather at any time between May and September.

Husk is usually controlled by vaccination though some anthelmintics are effective against lungworms. Cattle are vaccinated six weeks before turnout and again two weeks before (or at weaning in spring-born suckled calves weaned abruptly at grass). Calves should be at least two months old if they are to be vaccinated. This may not be possible with winter/spring-born calves in which case they should be dosed in July with an anthelmintic effective against lungworm.

CONSERVATION

Under British conditions silage is the best form of conservation because it gives a better balance between total yield and quality than hay, is less weather-sensitive and contributes to better overall grassland management. Machinery costs are higher than for haymaking but once the farm is tooled up (avoiding extravagant costs) grassland management and the quality of conserved forage are transformed. It is surprising therefore that it is only in comparatively recent years that silage has overtaken hay as the main conserved forage.

The factor which held back silage for many years was the inability to achieve consistently good fermentation quality. Now with a better understanding of the fermentation process and the availability of effective silage additives, experienced silage makers produce good quality feeds year after year. This has given them the confidence to cut earlier in the year when digestibility is high.

The kind of silage cattle like has high digestibility (D value over 63, ME at least 10 MJ/kg DM), a dry matter content of at least 25 per cent and a sweet-smelling lactic acid fermentation.

During the spring the yield of grass increases but digestibility declines. The rate of decline is about 0.5 unit of digestibility (D-value) per day

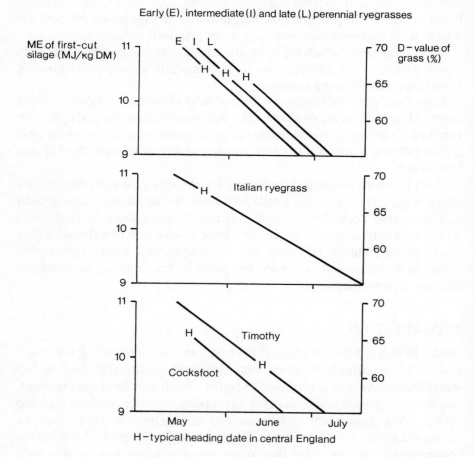

Fig. 7.2 General relationship between stage of growth, grass digestibility and silage quality.

through the cutting season. A conscious decision must therefore be made on the balance between D-value and yield. For finishing cattle the optimum balance is struck by cutting when D-values are in the range 63–67, but top silage makers aim even higher. For overwintered stores or spring-calving suckler cows an argument could be made for making lower quality silage. However, late cutting leaves a bare open stubble which takes a long time to recover, so it is better to aim for higher silage quality and to use lower quality feeds such as straw in designing rations with appropriate overall ME concentrations.

Seasonal changes in D-values for the main grass species and equivalent ME values for first-cut silage are shown for central England in Figure 7.2. These values would be reached about a week earlier in south west England, 10–14 days earlier in northern England and three weeks later in the north of Scotland. Pastures which have been grazed early in the season are usually in the 63–67D range a week later than ungrazed swards. In dry weather yield increases more slowly than usual and, to make matters worse, D-values fall faster than usual.

The stage of growth of the sward is related to changes in D-value but is not an infallible guide. Grass species and varieties vary in the point at which 67D is reached in relation to flower emergence. But for late heading varieties of perennial ryegrass 67D is reached just before the flower heads emerge.

Mixed swards have D-values dominated by the main grass species. Permanent pasture of good botanical composition will have a D-value profile similar to S23 ryegrass, perhaps with a slightly slower rate of seasonal fall. Legumes such as white clover slow down the rate of fall of D-value.

Regrowths are in the D-value range 63–67 for up to seven weeks in the case of perennial ryegrass but only five weeks for Italian ryegrass and cocksfoot.

An important conclusion from this analysis of D-values is that producing high quality silage requires a multiple cutting regime. A sward used only for conservation would be cut four times during the season, five times if ultra-high quality is the aim. Even where grazing and conservation are integrated, there are likely to be three silage-making campaigns during the season. Farm results recorded by MLC (Table 7.3) show that although more frequent cutting reduces first-cut yields as the date of first cut is brought forward, total silage yield increases with the number of cuts, of course at the expense of some increase in N fertiliser use. The late date of first cut in one and two cut regimes has a serious effect on nutritional quality.

Having decided the digestibility objective the next step is to make the silage with good control of fermentation and minimum losses. Good fermentation depends on high levels of sugar in the forage, strategic or

Table 7.3 Effect of frequency of cutting on silage yields. (Source: *MLC Beef Yearbook*, 1988.)

Cutting regime:	One cut	Two cuts	Three cuts	Four cuts
Date of first cut	24/6	12/6	24/5	19/5
– yield (tonnes/ha)	21	19	17	15
Date of second cut	—	8/8	9/7	1/7
– yield (tonnes/ha)		15	14	15
Date of third cut	—	—	2/9	14/8
– yield (tonnes/ha)	—	—	10	10
Date of fourth cut	—	—	—	6/10
– yield (tonnes/ha)	—	—	—	10
Total silage yield (tonnes/ha)	21	34	41	50
N fertiliser (kg N/ha)	152	202	294	395

routine use of silage additives and exclusion of air from the clamp. With good technique it should be possible to keep total dry matter loss from the original crop below 15 per cent. All too often, though, dry matter losses are 20 per cent or worse.

The best measure of silage fermentation is the amount of protein converted into ammonia. A value of ammonia N under 10 per cent of total N is good with 5 per cent excellent. Levels over 15 per cent are poor and anything above 20 per cent downright bad. At these higher levels of ammonia N the intake of silage by cattle is depressed (see Chapter 3).

Well fermented silages are necessarily acid and have pH values in the range 4.0–4.5. Bad silages with insufficient sugar or where air has got into the silo have high pH values which tend to drift upwards as clostridial bacteria break down lactic acid into evil-smelling butyric acid in an unstable silage. At the other extreme, well-fermented but wet silage can have very low pH values below 4 and down to 3.6. Intake can be disappointing and acidosis can occur so it may be advisable to feed sodium bicarbonate to reduce the acidity.

Good fermentation is the bacterial conversion of sugar into lactic acid which pickles the crop. Ideally, the sugar content of the crop at cutting should be at least 3 per cent. Italian and hybrid ryegrasses have higher sugar levels than perennial ryegrasses but clovers are rather low in sugar. Stage of growth also affects sugar content and early cut leafy material which is low both in sugar and dry matter is more difficult to make into good silage than more mature grass. Sugar levels are higher in sunny weather than on dull days and values peak in the afternoon.

Wilting cut grass for 24 hours in dry weather increases the sugar concentration by removing water. Also, if wilting is effective it speeds up carting grass to the silo because less water is carried about and reduces effluent loss from the silo which is an increasingly important environmental issue. Cattle eat more wilted than unwilted silage and in theory should perform better though research results are equivocal on this point. Overall there is a strong case for a 24-hour wilt aiming for a silage with at least 25 per cent dry matter. The wilting process can be speeded up by using a mower conditioner which increases water loss from the stems of grass. However, if wilting is not effective within 24 hours the grass should be carted nonetheless, otherwise field losses start to increase.

It goes almost without saying that during mowing and harvesting care should be taken to avoid soil contamination of the carted grass.

It is not always possible to mow grass for silage on a sunny afternoon to achieve high sugar levels or to get an effective wilt. Then the use of a silage additive should be considered. Indeed, many farmers use an additive routinely, arguing that the cost of £0.50–£1.50 per tonne is worthwhile to ensure good fermentation quality.

The traditional stand-by as a silage additive was molasses which added sugar. Latterly it has been supplanted by additives based on strong acids which augment the lactic acid produced by fermentation. Formalin has antimicrobial properties and is used in mixtures with acids to improve fermentation. In recent years microbial inoculants have been developed which add more efficient lactic acid bacteria than those occurring naturally. There are also enzyme products, sometimes combined with inoculants, which seek to produce sugars from cell wall constituents in the forage.

There is little doubt that formic acid applied at 2.5 litres per tonne when the grass is being picked up has proved itself the most effective additive. Sulphuric and propionic acids are also effective. The problem is that these acids are corrosive and dangerous to handle. Their salts are safer to handle but slower to act. It is the search for easily-handled additives which has focused interest on inoculants and enzymes. There are still reservations about the effectiveness of these novel products but several of them are now being used on farms to good effect.

Good fermentation also depends on the exclusion of air to cut down respiration which uses up precious sugar. A fairly short chop length of about 50 mm helps by facilitating consolidation (and releases sugar in the plant sap). Rolling after the silo is filled is greatly over-emphasised as the main method of consolidation. More effective is rapid filling and immediate sealing with a double polythene sheet which goes right down to the floor weighed down by old tyres. Even when filling is incomplete the sheet should be pulled over the clamp at night to exclude as much air as possible. In a clamp which is properly sealed the temperature during fermentation should not rise above 30°C, preferably lower. Careful attention to consolidation and sealing virtually eliminates top and side waste.

The lower the dry matter of the grass ensiled the greater will be the effluent loss. A 20 per cent dry matter silage can produce up to 100 litres effluent per tonne of grass, most of it in the first 10 days after filling the silo. Above 25 per cent dry matter there is little or no effluent. Effluent is undesirable because it smells awful, is a nuisance to handle, represents a loss of feed value and is a dangerous pollutant. Some farmers collect their fresh effluent and feed it but more often it is collected in a storage tank and spread on the land.

A good deal of recent attention has been paid to absorbents such as sugar beet pulp or proprietary products mixed at about 50 kg per tonne of 20 per cent dry matter forage during filling of the silo. Mixing is a tedious extra job at the busy clamp but absorbents do reduce effluent and may improve fermentation by adding extra sugar.

When the clamp is fed (at least three weeks after filling) management of the silage face has an important bearing on wastage caused by secondary fermentation and moulding. These are a particular problem in warm summer weather. A fairly narrow face is ideal so that the feed face moves back noticeably each day. Also, the use of a block cutter to remove silage keeps the face smooth and limits spoilage.

Big bale silage is one of the finest ever farmer inventions and, using contractors, is applicable on farms without silage-making facilities or equipment, for conserving small quantities of grass, or for extra conservation when the clamps are full. The 1.2 m diameter bales are made from unchopped grass picked up by the baler from a mown swath; the grass may or may not be wilted. The bales are either fitted into a black polythene bag tied securely at the neck or wrapped with several layers of polythene film using special equipment. Wrapping is preferable, despite its higher cost, because there is better exclusion of air and wrapped bales are less susceptible to vermin and gale damage than bags.

Big bale silage rarely approaches the quality of the best clamp silage but big bales are so convenient on many farms that over 10 million are made annually in Great Britain.

INTEGRATION OF GRAZING AND CONSERVATION

Adopting grazing stocking rates which control sward heights within

Fig. 7.3 Integration of grazing and conservation in 18-month beef using the 1-2-3 system. (Source: ICI.)

recommended ranges and silage cutting regimes which produce the required amount of silage are distinct targets each in its own right. But the integration of grazing and conservation is an aid to meeting both targets.

Adopting high grazing stocking rates early in the season releases a higher proportion of the grassland for first-cut silage. And multiple silage cuts release a sequence of fresh aftermaths which are available for grazing if required. Grass growth is so compressed into early summer that it is usual to conserve between half and two thirds of the grassland area in May. About a third of the area should be available for a second cut of silage.

This arrangement was formalised by Imperial Chemical Industries (ICI) in the 1–2–3 system of grassland management for 18-month beef illustrated in Figure 7.3. The cattle graze a third of the grassland area to mid-season

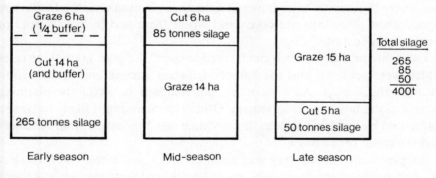

Assumptions:

20 ha – 250 kg N per ha – 4 cattle per ha overall

80 cattle stocked weighing: 180 kg at turnout
                             260 kg in mid-season
                             340 kg in late season

Grazing stocking rates: 2.5 tonnes per ha in early season
                         2.0 tonnes per ha in mid-season
                         1.7 tonnes per ha in late season

Fig. 7.4 Model of integrated grazing and conservation in 18-month beef.

with the other two-thirds conserved as first-cut silage. In mid-July the cattle are moved onto the silage aftermath for grazing and the original grazing area is conserved. Then in late summer cattle graze the whole area.

In recent years the system has been refined with the addition of a buffer grazing area and higher grazing stocking rates are adopted which may allow a third cut of silage to be taken from part of the area. For example, overall stocking rates recorded by MLC in 18-month beef units averaged nearly 4 cattle per hectare in 1988 compared to about 3 when ICI originally proposed the 1–2–3 system. The present approach is modelled as an example in Figure 7.4.

For other types of beef production the precise balance between grazing and conservation may vary at different stages of the grazing season. But grassland utilisation should always be planned by setting target weights of cattle stocked on the grazing area through the season and allocating a sufficient area for silage requirements to be produced. Then silage aftermaths should be used to the full for grazing as the season progresses.

RECORDING GRASSLAND OUTPUT

Almost every beef producer counts grazing cattle, but only as a check that they are all alive and well, not as part of a systematic recording system. It is not a very big step to write down in a diary cattle numbers, the fields they graze, when silage cuts are taken and where from and to keep a note of fertiliser applications.

Later on, the diary records can be used to check the grazing stocking rates which were achieved and the balance between grazing and conservation through the season. As a recorded experience it is useful for planning grassland management next season. Otherwise planning is likely to be too influenced by incidents such as 'the dry time last June when grass ran short and the cattle broke out'.

Simple records are all very well when there is a single beef enterprise but often there are several batches of grazing cattle and there may also be sheep or dairy cows. In fact records are even more valuable in a complex situation. The easiest way to handle different categories of stock is to multiply numbers by their average weight to find the total weight stocked. This is much easier than using the old livestock unit systems which tried to equate one class of stock with another.

It is also worth making a check on the actual quantity of silage in store rather than risking the expensive realisation late in the winter that the nominal estimate was over-optimistic. For clamp silage measure the height of silage, clamp width, the length at full height and the length of the sloping wedge at the front of the clamp. Volume is then height × width × length of the full height section of the clamp plus half the height × width × length of the sloping wedge. To find the tonnage of silage volume is multiplied by density which, for short-chopped material in a clamp with a face 2–3 metres high, ranges from about 0.75 tonnes per cubic metre at 20 per cent silage dry matter, to 0.66 tonnes at 25 per cent and 0.62 tonnes at 30 per cent dry matter.

Knowledge of the weight of cattle stocked month by month through the grazing season, the amount of silage made, the total area of grassland utilised and fertiliser inputs is good enough in most situations to assess grassland output.

For a more sophisticated evaluation, dairy farming advisers have developed the Utilised Metabolisable Energy (UME) system. It is an estimate of the ME from grass which is actually eaten by the cattle.

The annual ME requirement of an animal is calculated and from this is deducted the ME provided by concentrates and other feeds to calculate the ME from grass. Multiplied by the stocking rate this gives the UME per hectare. Top dairy herds achieve UME outputs around 100,000 MJ per hectare usually expressed as 100 gigajoules (GJ where 1 GJ = 1000 MJ). This would only be rivalled in the beef sector by grass silage beef with its intensive grassland management.

8 Marketing

Marketing has grabbed the headlines for years and probably no word has been more abused and misused. To most farmers marketing is simply the act of selling their cattle. At the other extreme marketing is regarded by some people as synonymous with meat promotion and advertising. All-pervading is the mistaken view that marketing is something which happens 'beyond the farm gate'.

The objective here is to present marketing as the business of sales management 'through the farm gate'. It involves product specification, live cattle evaluation and carcase classification, marketing methods and price reporting which clearly identifies quality differentials. The whole process should be dedicated to supplying consumer demand.

THE MARKET

In developed countries the market is evolving rapidly to a situation where the number of farmers stays much the same or falls slowly but the number of buyers is declining rapidly as meat businesses become larger, and therefore fewer, and retail sales are dominated increasingly by supermarket chains.

Table 8.1 Source of purchase of beef and veal in Great Britain. (Source: *MLC Meat Demand Trends.*)

	1978	1980	1982	1984	1986	1988
	Percentage					
Butchers	63.7	61.1	60.2	57.4	51.4	44.9
Co-ops	5.6	6.2	5.4	5.5	6.2	5.4
Supermarkets	17.0	19.1	21.5	23.8	28.1	32.9
Independent grocers	3.3	3.0	2.8	2.5	2.2	2.5
Freezer centres	3.3	3.2	3.8	3.2	4.0	3.9
Other outlets	7.0	7.5	6.3	7.5	8.2	10.5

Table 8.2 Trends in meat consumption.
(Source: MAFF, *MLC Beef Yearbook*.)

	Beef and veal	Mutton and lamb	Pork	Bacon	Poultry
	(kg carcase weight per head)				
1950	21.2	11.4	2.0	9.7	2.5
1960	21.4	11.1	8.7	11.3	5.3
1970	21.4	9.6	11.1	11.4	10.7
1980	20.5	7.5	12.5	9.0	13.4
1982	18.3	7.3	12.9	8.4	14.4
1984	18.3	6.8	12.6	8.3	15.6
1986	19.3	6.4	12.8	8.1	17.2
1988	18.9	6.4	14.3	7.9	19.4

Table 8.1 shows just how quickly retail sales are moving towards the supermarkets at the expense of independent butchers.

These changes need to be looked at in relation to trends in consumption patterns. Table 8.2 shows that beef and veal consumption has been more stable than is commonly supposed with a slight rise through the mid-1980s, though the long-term trend is slowly downwards. However, there has been a switch in the pattern of consumption with an increasing proportion of beef eaten out of the home as restaurant steaks – Britain's favourite food – roasts and beefburgers (Table 8.3). So domestic purchases have declined as a proportion of total consumption. ˙

The most striking change in meat consumption is the increase in poultry meat (Table 8.2) from a Christmas speciality to a high volume year-round product; pork consumption also increased between 1950 and 1970 but is now steady. Conversely, lamb consumption is falling.

Table 8.3 Domestic purchases of beef and veal.
(Source: *National Food Survey*.)

	Total supplies (thousand tonnes carcase weight)	Household consumption (thousand tonnes product weight)
1980	1200	441
1982	1058	400
1984	1042	390
1986	1118	394
1988	1103	355

MARKET REQUIREMENTS

The market for meat has evolved rapidly over recent years and is still changing. Modern lifestyles with less time spent in the kitchen favour convenience cuts, prepared meals and eating out. With the growth of the 'green movement' there is concern about the safety and wholesomeness of food and the ethics of meat production. Vegetarian activists easily command media coverage with their attacks on the meat eating habit. On the other wing of opinion is a significant group of consumers who really like beef and are prepared to pay a substantial premium for high quality.

The market for meat appears to be segmenting. The main demand is for regular beef judged as much on price as on quality. Then there is a demand for a traditional high quality product such as Scotch beef, for home consumption and export. And finally, there are special niche markets for beef which is 'additive-free' or 'organic'. In the development of the market it is important that promotion of small volume 'niche' products is not at the expense of regular beef.

Overlying social factors affecting the beef market is a concern for healthy living promoted by the Government to reduce premature death from heart disease. For example, the 1984 report by the UK Government's Committee on Medical Aspects of Food Policy, euphemistically known as the COMA report, made the following recommendations:

- Eat less fat, particularly saturated fat.
- Eat less salt.
- Eat less sugar.
- Drink less alcohol.
- Consume more fibre.
- Stop smoking.
- Watch blood pressure.
- Take regular exercise.
- Control weight.
- Obtain more nutrients through 'whole' foods.

Particular attention has been focused on the advice to eat less saturated fat and the crude interpretation of this by the media and many so-called experts who should know better was 'eat less meat'. However, the meat industry interpretation to 'eat leaner meat' seems to have found its mark, though continual publicity is required to reinforce the message.

The meat industry campaign was justified because in the UK diet beef accounts for only 4 per cent of total fat, 4 per cent of saturated fat and 3 per cent of energy intake. On the positive side beef provides 7 per cent of protein intake and is an important source of B vitamins (especially B_{12}), iron and trace minerals.

The diet and health issue has merely accelerated an existing demand trend towards leaner meat. The pace of this trend has been misjudged by some farmers and butchers who see the end-point as ultra-lean beef of poor eating quality. The discussion of carcase classification results in Chapter 2 shows that so far the main effect has been a reduction in the proportion of above average fat class 4H and an increase in below average fat class 3 but with average fat 4L still the most common class. This is in line with the market where meat buyers penalise overfat 4H carcases. However, considerations of eating quality (see Chapter 2) do imply that fatness should not fall below fat class 3. The demand for extra lean cuts of beef by the most fastidious consumers can still be met by fat trimming during retail preparation.

Whether cattle are sold deadweight or by live auction there are considerable price differentials for conformation, much higher than for fatness. Price penalties are particularly severe for carcases classifying -0 or worse (which failed to qualify for subsidy payments under the variable

	1	2	3	4L	4H	5L	5H
E	Base + 10						
U+ −U	Base + 6				Base		
R	Base						
O+	Base − 4						
−O	Base − 12						
P+ −P	Base − 20						

(p/kg deadweight)

Weight penalties   Under 220 kg } − 3p
                  Over   320 kg

Fig. 8.1 Example deadweight price schedule.

premium scheme, discontinued in 1989). These penalties are out of all proportion to the significance of poor conformation either to meat yield or the attractiveness of retail cuts. Premiums at the upper end of the conformation scale are usually smaller than penalties at the lower end, particularly in deadweight price schedules. An example price schedule is shown in Figure 8.1.

The differentials paid for conformation are justified at least in part by the smaller increase in saleable meat yield as conformation improves due to higher muscle:bone ratios. In addition the meat trade argues that with good conformation the carcase can be butchered to better advantage.

The meat trade has become preoccupied with conformation during the 1980s when, as shown in Chapter 1, the proportion of dairy beef was increasing and conformation was deteriorating because of the impact of specialised dairy Holsteins from North America. Now with a much higher level of beef crossing in dairy herds, mainly to continental breeds of good conformation, and an increase in the proportion of suckler beef, conformation is improving again.

In addition to fatness and conformation, buyers have preferred weight ranges for cattle/carcases. There is a broad middle band from about 240 kg to 300+ kg carcase weight which is acceptable to most buyers, but some prefer lightweight carcases and pay accordingly. A few buyers will handle very heavy carcases but once weights go above 310–320 kg a price penalty is imposed by the majority of buyers.

For many years steers have commanded a higher price per kg than heifers, typically 2–4p per kg liveweight. However, through 1988 when slaughter cattle were in short supply the price difference narrowed considerably. There have always been butchers who preferred heifer beef, usually on the (unproven) argument that it eats better than steer beef.

Despite resistance to bull beef in many sectors of the UK meat trade, it has commanded a premium over steer beef, probably reflecting the higher meat yield from lean bull carcases.

A general knowledge of market requirements and the preferences of particular buyers is extremely important to the producer, not only in the selection of breed or cross, sex and production system, but also in directing cattle to the market outlet where they will sell to best advantage.

MARKETING METHODS

Normally the choice in marketing methods facing the producer is between selling cattle through a live auction market or direct to a deadweight buyer.

An agent or livestock marketing group may act as an intermediary.

Live auction supporters argue the merits of prices being determined by public competition between buyers. And if prices are considered not good enough the producer can withdraw cattle from the sale to be offered again on another occasion. Producers argue that time is well spent at the market because of the business done and the peripheral information gathered.

Committed deadweight sellers argue that their method of selling is convenient, prices are more stable than in the auction, payment is on carcase weight so killing-out percentage is taken out of pricing and quality differentials are defined by reference to the carcase classification grid. No time is wasted attending markets and telephone contact with the buyer gives all the information needed on market requirements.

The problem with the live auction is that undeniably large quality differentials are paid, but because there is no formal evaluation of the quality of cattle in UK markets the price reports do not indicate what the differentials were. The only way to find out is to attend the market.

The problem would be overcome if through a system of cattle identification carcase results could be passed back to the producer and to auctioneers for price reporting. The possibility of a national identification scheme has been discussed in terms of an electronic system but as yet the equipment has not been quite good enough to prompt action. Farmers are unlikely to pay for an expensive electronic system which identifies cattle no more than a few feet away when they can purchase much cheaper ear tags which can be read yards away. And Government is rapidly withdrawing from all funding of this type. This is a pity since a national identification scheme has relevance not just to marketing but to health control and genetic improvement as well.

The problems of establishing a national scheme need not inhibit local schemes by which carcase results could be passed back to finishers and beyond to the suckler herds which bred the cattle.

Some auctioneers have argued for the evaluation of cattle before sale using the terms of the EEC beef carcase classification scheme. This would be a service to buyers and would make price reports much more revealing. At last auction markets are beginning to use a visual/handling method of evaluation before sale. A subjective method such as this will always be open to criticism but there is hope of developing velocity of sound equipment (see Chapter 2) which is quick and easy to use and displays an estimate of percentage lean or fat class in the auction ring.

Critics of deadweight selling point to the few UK buyers who actually publish their buying specifications, the incomprehensible presentation of information in some published price schedules and differences in conditions of purchase which make it difficult to compare bottom-line prices. Prices are said to be slow to respond when market prices are rising and, as has already been mentioned, premiums are small or non-existent at the upper end of the conformation range.

The ability to compare live auction and deadweight prices is important to farmers deciding on their marketing route, to buyers of live cattle in deciding their bids and to deadweight buyers drawing up price schedules.

Comparison is notoriously difficult, mainly because killing-out percentage is difficult to estimate. Weight losses in cattle vary according to the distance they travel and the time they are held at market before sale.

Preliminary results of an MLC trial (*1988 Beef Yearbook*, MLC) showed that weight losses occurred mainly during transport. Weight at the local auction averaged about 20 kg below the ex-farm weight. Cattle taken direct from farm to the abattoir and slaughtered immediately killed out 0.8 per cent higher than those routed via an auction market and held in the abattoir lairage overnight before slaughter.

Marketing methods are slow to change but just as computers and telecommunications have revolutionised the world's financial markets they also have potential in cattle marketing.

Computer Aided Livestock Marketing (CALM) in Australia and the Ontario Livestock Exchange (OLEX) in Canada use modern information technology allied to traditional skills in a new approach to marketing. The schemes differ in detail but both have the same essential feature which is that cattle on farms are sold by remote bidding without having to go to market.

The first step is on-farm evaluation of carcase quality, either by the farmer himself or by an agent of the marketing organisation. Evaluation skills are checked against final carcase results and are kept sharp because buyers can impose price penalties if discrepancies are outside agreed limits.

Details of cattle for sale are held on a central computer which is linked to screens and keyboards in buyers' offices. At the time of the sale an executive of the marketing organisation acts as market manager. The sale order of lots of cattle is balloted and details of the number, their breed, weight and estimated carcase type are displayed on buyers' screens. The buyers then key in their bids and bidding stops after an agreed time lapse with no further bid. At the end of the sale the buyer arranges with the farmer for delivery of the cattle. Payment is on actual weight and grade and carcase details are passed back to the farmer.

Inevitably a successful remote bidding system would be competitive with the auction market. Yet, if as seems likely, auctioneers ran remote bidding alongside their existing auction businesses, the two systems could co-exist. This is certainly how the first British system 'Electronic Auction Systems Europe' which is based on OLEX has been initiated.

The way in which producers can gain strength as sellers is to market cooperatively. Livestock marketing cooperatives aim to increase bargaining power through the volume of sales they control and the ability to provide a level supply of specified quality. In this way cooperatives aim to provide greater market security, more stable prices and – hopefully – improved returns. With a handful of notable exceptions cooperatives have never gained the strength in Britain that they have in continental Europe. It seems that British farmers are not prepared to surrender personal independence in favour of collective strength.

The lack of commitment to cooperative marketing has left room for several commercial marketing companies to develop. These act as brokers between farmers and meat businesses using volume and continuity of supply to negotiate premium prices which give the farmer a fair return and leave commission for the marketing company. There is always the danger that, under pressure to fill orders, the marketing company presses farmers to sell cattle without their best interests sufficiently in mind.

Some experts hold the view that vertical integration is the most likely outcome of the increasing dominance of large supermarket companies with a handful of large meat plants supplying them. Either the meat plant or the retailer would determine cattle type, production system and carcase type, probably supplying some of the inputs. The farmer would be contracted to supply land, buildings and management skills.

Vertical integration is already common in poultry production and happens to a lesser extent in pig production. Perhaps it is less likely in a smaller scale, land-using enterprise such as beef. But it is inevitable that to supply their increasingly demanding quality specifications buyers will become involved as far back along the production/marketing chain as necessary.

LIVE CATTLE EVALUATION

Whether sold liveweight or deadweight the decision to market is always taken on live cattle on the farm. Therefore the ability to evaluate likely carcase quality in live cattle is vital to successful marketing.

As yet there is no ultrasonic equipment cheap enough for use by the producer on the farm, so a handling/visual method must be used. With practice it should be possible to predict carcase classes correctly for more than half the cattle and not more than one conformation or one fat class out for the remainder.

It is important that cattle are evaluated systematically using visual

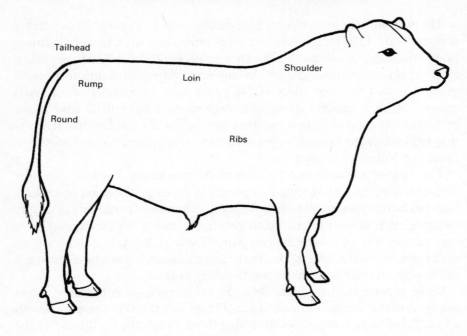

Tailhead

Shoulder

Loin

Rump

Round

Ribs

Fig. 8.2 Handling and inspection points for the evaluation of conformation and fatness.

inspection to assess conformation and handling to assess fatness (Figure 8.2). Visual inspection is best done when cattle are standing naturally in a collecting pen. If possible, handle cattle from the left ('open') side as seen from behind to avoid interference at the loin from the kidney knob and channel fat which projects further forward on the right side.

In the visual evaluation of conformation cattle of good shape are thickly muscled with a rounded shape whilst those of poor shape are thinly muscled and angular. Conformation is assessed at the round, rump and loin/ shoulder area (Table 8.4).

Evaluating fatness is the more difficult job and there is no substitute for handling cattle in a race or crush. The key handling points are the ribs, loin and tailhead (Figure 8.2). In cattle of good conformation class –U or better the thickness of muscling over the loin makes this an unreliable handling point. Fatness evaluation is described in Table 8.5.

Cattle evaluation skills need to be checked continually and for dead-weight sales the best way of doing this is to keep a record of the on-farm evaluation and compare it with actual carcase classification returns.

Table 8.4 Guidelines for the visual evaluation of conformation.

Conformation class	Round	Rump	Loin/shoulder
E	Double muscled or nearly so	Very wide, mid-line in hollow	Thickly muscled, mid-line in hollow
U+	Thick, well rounded	Very wide, level through mid-line	Very wide, mid-line in hollow
-U	Quite thick, well rounded	Wide, slight slope away from mid-line	Wide, mid-line in slight hollow
R	Distinctly rounded	Quite wide, slight slope away from mid-line	Wide, level through mid-line
O+	Slightly rounded	Rather narrow, slight slope away from mid-line	Rather narrow, slight slope away from mid-line
-O	No rounding, straight profile	Narrow, distinct slope away from mid-line	Narrow, distinct slope away from mid-line
P	Hollow profile	Very narrow, sharp slope away from mid-line	Very narrow, sharp slope away from mid-line

PLANNED BEEF PRODUCTION AND MARKETING

Table 8.5 Guidelines on handling for the evaluation of fatness.

Handle from left side
Ribs – press with flat of hand to feel soft fat between hide and firm muscle.
Loin – grip loin with thumb and forefinger and feel fat over bony outer edge of loin.
Tailhead – press with fingers to feel fat.

Conformation class R or poorer			Fat class	Fat thickness (mm)	Conformation class –U or better	
Ribs	Loin	Tailhead			Ribs	Tailhead
Bony ribs, no fat	Bony, no fat	No fat	1	1	Ribs felt with moderate pressure, no fat.	No fat
Ribs visible, little fat	Bony, little fat	No fat	2	2	Ribs felt with moderate pressure, little fat.	No fat
Ribs just visible, slight fat	Bone felt easily, slight fat	Slight fat	3	3	Ribs felt with firm pressure, slight fat	Slight fat
Ribs felt with light pressure, moderate fat	Bone felt with light pressure, moderate fat	Moderate fat	4L	4–5	Ribs difficult to feel, moderate fat	Moderate fat
Ribs felt with firm pressure, thick fat	Bone felt with firm pressure	Puffy fat	4H	6–7	Ribs cannot be felt, thick fat	Puffy fat
Very fat	Very fat	Very fat	5L/5H	8+	Very fat	Very fat

PLANNED MARKETING

In developing a marketing plan it is important to appreciate that the objective is to maximise profit not merely to achieve the highest price per kg or the greatest total return. This means taking account of accumulating production costs and interest charges as well as increasing returns.

There are four steps in developing the marketing plan:

(1) Forecast price trends and evaluate alternative buying specifications and conditions of purchase.
(2) Predict cattle performance.
(3) Predict production costs.
(4) Develop a marketing plan which maximises profit.

Prices

Price forecasting is notoriously difficult but is essential to the marketing plan given that cattle may be sold over a period of several weeks. Where alternative deadweight price schedules are available these should be compared, taking full account of the effect of quality and weight on prices as well as all deductions. If liveweight and deadweight selling are options, remember when comparing prices that ex-farm liveweight is likely to be about 20 kg heavier than auction market weight.

The following killing-out percentages can be used to calculate carcase weight from an on-farm weight:

Friesian/Holstein	53
Angus and Hereford crosses	54
Charolais and Simmental crosses	55
Limousin crosses	56

If quality differentials are not quoted in auction market reports the only sensible assumption is that they are similar to deadweight differentials. Price adjustments are necessary for bulls, steers and heifers using information from price reports.

Predict cattle performance

Knowledge of the level of cattle performance being achieved is very important in developing a marketing plan. On a given type of ration the faster cattle grow the greater is the margin over feed costs and the higher the optimum slaughter weight, provided cattle still meet the buyers' specification.

As well as knowing the average performance of a pen of cattle, it is also necessary to know individual performance because fast growers are likely to have a higher optimum slaughter weight than slow growers. Therefore it is important to weigh cattle periodically during the finishing period, not only as a check on management, but also to help in drawing up the marketing plan.

Conventional wisdom is that as cattle move into the final stages of finishing, rate of fattening increases sharply and daily gain and feed conversion efficiency fall dramatically. It is now becoming apparent that rate of fattening is not as rapid as is commonly supposed. It takes at least six weeks for cattle to traverse an EEC fat class. In fact daily gain and feed conversion efficiency fall quite slowly during the final stages of finishing.

The variation of individual performance of cattle within a pen is considerable. The usual practice is to market fast growers first as soon as they enter the buyer's weight range but to retain slow growers, hoping that they will improve. It is this practice which causes the impression that performance deteriorates rapidly because average pen performance is determined increasingly by the poorer cattle which are left behind.

It would pay better to retain the fast growers longer (provided they do not slip into a penalty fat class or weight range) because they have the potential to use feed profitably. On the other hand, slow growers should be marketed sooner, before they start losing money, unless they are just about to enter a higher price bracket. The overall effect of such a strategy is usually to shorten the marketing period.

Predict production costs

Production costs include feed, bedding, any miscellaneous items and interest charges.

Feed is by far the most important component of variable costs and simple feed records are extremely valuable in providing information on daily feed costs. For silage it is probably wise to use the total cost, which is in the range £15–£20 per tonne on most farms, rather than the variable cost convention of gross margin costings.

The lower daily gains of slow growers are explained in the large part by lower intake of the *ad libitum* components of the ration. When drawing up a marketing plan for cattle within a pen at different performance levels the simplest approach is to assume that feed intake is in proportion to weight. So if the average intake of 450 kg cattle is 25 kg silage, cattle of 400 kg would be calculated to eat 22 kg and those of 500 kg, 28 kg. When the marketing plan involves a change from the usual sale date it is important to work out a feed budget to see whether there are sufficient feed supplies to carry the plan through.

Bedding costs are commonly forgotten or under-estimated and it is important that these are included in the calculation with straw at its farmgate sale value or purchase price.

Moving sale dates in time has effects on cash flow and so interest charges should be calculated on the value of cattle at alternative market end-points.

Marketing plan

Drawing up the marketing plan is done by putting together the information on calculated returns and production costs to find the sale date on which the financial margin is maximised.

The first job is to go through the cattle just before marketing is expected to begin, weighing them and evaluating conformation and fatness. Then sale returns are calculated over 10–20 day periods, taking account of increasing weight and any weight-related price bands, predicted changes in conformation and fatness and seasonal price trends. It is important to remember that these differentials apply to the total weight of the animal and can have much bigger effects on total returns than seems possible at first sight. The calculated values of cattle can be used to generate approximate interest charges. And, finally, total feed, bedding and miscellaneous costs for the 10–20 day periods, together with interest charges, are deducted from the increase in returns to calculate the additional margin earned. The point at which there is no longer a margin over costs is the optimum sale date.

This calculated sale date should not be adhered to slavishly. Rather, cattle should be weighed and handled regularly during the marketing period and sold when they actually attain the market end-point.

An example marketing plan for cereal beef bulls is shown in Table 8.6 with calculations for the fast and slow growers within the pen. The performance values are notional but are typical of those seen in commercial practice. They show that, despite the large differences in performance, differences in daily feed intake and hence costs are quite small.

For the fast growers, financial margins for 20-day periods keep edging up right until the point where the overweight penalty is imposed. At the other end of the scale margins for slow growers jump when they move above the minimum weight but then slump into loss. In either case it is worth retaining

Table 8.6 Example marketing plan for cereal beef bulls.

	Days:	0	20	40	60	80
Performance						
(a) Fast growers						
Daily gain (kg)			1.50	1.45	1.40	1.35
Daily feed (kg)			10.0	9.9	9.8	9.8
Liveweight (kg)		450	480	508	536	568
Estimated carcase weight (kg)		248	264	279	295	310
(b) Slow growers						
Daily gain (kg)			1.20	1.15	1.10	1.05
Daily feed (kg)			9.3	9.2	9.1	9.1
Liveweight (kg)		375	399	422	444	465
Estimated carcase weight (kg)		206	219	232	244	256

Values

(a) Buyer's specification
(p/kg carcase)

		Fat class			Weight
		2	3	4L	penalties:
Conformation	–U		Base + 5		
	R		Base (225p)		Under 220 kg –3p
					Over 300 kg –3p
	O+		Base –5		

Assume no seasonal price trend

(b) Fast growers

	Days:	0	20	40	60	80
Sale value (£)	–U	570	607	642	679	704*
	R	558	594	628	664	688*
	O+	546	581	614	649	673*
						* overweight deduction

(c) Slow growers

Sale value (£)	–U	468**	497**	534	561	589
	R	457**	486**	522	549	576
	O+	447**	475**	510	537	563
						** underweight deduction

Table 8.6 *(Contd)*

Days:	0–20	20–40	40–60	60–80
Costs				
(a) Fast growers				
Feed @ £120 per tonne	24	24	24	24
Other costs	2	2	2	2
Bank interest	5	6	6	6
Total costs	31	32	32	32
(b) Slow growers				
Feed @ £120 per tonne	22	22	22	22
Other costs	2	2	2	2
Bank interest	4	5	5	5
Total costs	28	29	29	29
Marginal costing				
(a) Fast growers				
Increase in value (£)				
−U	37	35	37	25
R3	36	34	36	24
O+3	35	33	35	24
Costs	31	32	32	32
				sell
(b) Slow growers				
Increase in value (£)				
−U3	29	37	27	28
R3	29	36	27	27
O+3	28	35	27	26
Costs (£)	28	29	29	29
		sell		

an animal which is definitely on the verge of the higher conformation class to earn the significant premium involved.

In this particular example with the same price for fat classes 2, 3 and 4L, fat class does not need to be taken into account for lean bulls. However, for plans involving steers and heifers fat class becomes important since most buyers pay lower prices when cattle slip into 4H.

It might be argued that such a marketing plan is designed solely with the producer's profit in mind, without proper regard to the buyer's requirements. On the contrary, both producer and buyer could benefit from this approach. The buyer receives the best quality cattle at the upper end of his preferred weight range and less desirable types at the lower end of the range. This is far preferable to the reverse situation which tends to exist at present. Moreover, armed with a knowledge of the structure of marketing plans the buyer can adjust price differentials to target cattle more precisely to his needs.

QUALITY SPECIFICATIONS

An important development in meat marketing is the creation of wide-ranging quality specifications designed to achieve consistent product appearance, safety, wholesomeness and good eating quality.

In some cases the specifications are being developed by supermarkets and butchery chains for their own supply. Elsewhere, specifications are being developed at meat plants to supply beef of consistent specification to retailers.

The key aspects of these specifications operate within meat plants and are concerned with slaughter and dressing procedures and chilling and hanging regimes for meat. There is also a consumer aspect with improved labelling of cuts to promote good cookery practice so that eating quality is not impaired. But in addition, looking back through the farm gate there will be parts of the overall specification of significance to producers.

The production specification will include the production system, age at slaughter, breed or cross, sex, conformation and fat class and pre-slaughter handling to avoid dark cutting. Some specifications may go further in defining niche products from cattle reared without growth promoters or by 'organic' methods.

The implications of these quality specifications is that producers and the meat trade alike will have to take a much more disciplined approach to the production and marketing of beef.

9   Calf Rearing

The majority of dairy-bred calves for beef rearing are sold at 10–20 days of age to specialist calf rearers and dairy beef producers. Changing farms, they are sensitive to disease even if they have received adequate colostrum. And, if they have been sold through an auction market, as the majority are, they are stressed when they arrive at the rearer's farm.

Success in calf rearing has more to do with getting calves through the first three months alive and healthy than achieving the highest daily gains.

In calf rearing units recorded by MLC, average calf mortality is about 4 per cent but in the bottom third of units it is twice as high. The target should be mortality rates below 3 per cent with a low incidence of the two scourges of calf rearing – enteritis and pneumonia.

Calf rearing is such a specialised job that in recent years it has become possible for dairy beef producers to purchase reared calves at three months of age from specialist rearers. The beef producer forgoes the calf rearer's margin but avoids the tricky job of rearing and probably buys a better calf than could have been reared on the farm.

The calf rearing system needs to recognise the fundamental physiological development taking place in the calf from simple digestion in the true stomach (abomasum) to full ruminant function of the rumen, reticulum and omasum. The most cost-effective rearing system is early weaning which was pioneered in Britain and hastens the onset of rumen function. Calves are fed a limited quantity of milk replacer for about five weeks and are weaned when they are consuming just sufficient concentrate to be independent of milk. Pre-weaning growth rates are relatively low but daily gains pick up rapidly after weaning.

COLOSTRUM

The greatest service the dairy farmer can render to the calf rearer is to ensure that calves receive colostrum within a few hours of birth. This is because colostrum contains the immune lactoglobulins and their associated antibodies which confer on the calf passive immunity to disease. To provide immunity these protein lactoglobulins must be absorbed intact from the small intestine into the blood stream and the ability to do this lasts only about 24 hours.

Calves which receive no colostrum have poor survival prospects and low intakes predispose them to disease. Either the calf should remain with the cow for 12 hours, ensuring that suckling is normal, or colostrum should be fed from a bucket. The aim should be an intake of at least 4 litres of colostrum during the first day of life.

Blood serum from calves which have received colostrum gives a turbid reaction when mixed with zinc sulphate solution and this is sometimes used as a routine colostrum test to identify calves which need special care.

Colostrum is also a highly digestible first feed for calves rich in digestible protein, minerals and the fat-soluble vitamins A, D and E. If it is available colostrum should continue to be fed instead of milk replacer.

CALF RECEPTION

The reception procedure described here is for purchased calves but the main management points are equally important for the homebred calf.

There should be two weeks at least between batches of calves to limit the carry-over of disease and cleaning should be carried out as soon as pens are vacated by the previous batch of calves not just before the next batch arrive. The buildings and penning should be power-washed, or if possible steam-cleaned, and disinfected. Feeding equipment should also be thoroughly cleaned and disinfected. The pens (see Chapter 6 for dimensions) should be bedded deeply with clean, dry barley straw.

Calves should be examined one at a time before they are unloaded and only those accepted which are alert, bright-eyed, clean-nosed, have a pencil-thin naval (which is dipped in iodine solution to prevent navel ill) and no sign of scouring. The calves should be weighed, fitted with an easily-read plastic ear tag and moved without further fuss into their pens.

After the calves have been penned they should be fed not with milk replacer but a warm drink of electrolyte solution at about 40°C. If the calves will not drink from a bucket try a bottle fitted with a teat but do not force them. The electrolyte may be a proprietary product or a home mix of 60 g glucose and 20 g salt dissolved in 2 litres of warm water at about 40°C.

Homebred calves can be fed milk replacer from the time they are separated from the cow, though it is sensible to feed colostrum for as long as it is possible.

Within the first 24 hours calves should be given a multivitamin product either by injection or in the first milk feed. If there are signs of lice sprinkle delousing powder/liquid on the calves.

CALFHOOD DISEASES

Enteritis causing scouring and pneumonia are the two most important calfhood diseases. When calves die the loss is only too obvious. But disease has a high cost for the survivors too, not only because of the veterinary and farm staff costs of treating sick calves, but also because of the carry-over effects on later performance. Daily gains are depressed permanently, extending the feeding period and increasing production costs.

Early recognition of disease symptoms is the mark of good stockmanship. Anyone can point out a calf with a raging infection but it is the observant calf rearer who spots the earlier signs – dullness, unease, hanging back from feed – which signal the onset of disease but allow treatment in time to prevent severe illness.

Enteritis

Scouring due to *Escherichia coli* is a major cause of illness and mortality in milk-fed calves during the first two or three weeks. It is at its worst in the spring because of the build-up of infection over-winter.

Slightly loose faeces are quite normal early on in the milk feeding period but if the calf is overfed it develops into more persistent nutritional scouring which can be the prelude to infectious scour. The milk feeding regimes described later are designed to prevent over-feeding.

If scouring persists for more than 24 hours and the calf is unwell the first action should be to withdraw milk and feed a warm electrolyte solution to prevent dehydration in the calf. If the calf develops a high temperature (over 39.5°C) veterinary advice should be sought to decide what, if any, antibiotic treatment is appropriate. (Routine treatment with antibiotic is not recommended except on veterinary advice because of the risk of build-up of resistant strains of infectious bacteria.)

As calves return to normal milk replacer should be reintroduced gradually over two or three days.

Scouring caused by Salmonella is particularly vicious and causes considerable mortality. Two bacteria are involved, *Salmonella typhimurium* which is zoonotic, i.e. it can infect humans, and *S. dublin*. The organisms can survive off the calf for a considerable time so residual infection in buildings and cattle lorries is a problem, and older cattle can be carriers.

Salmonellosis usually strikes when calves are about three weeks old and can spread to older weaned calves. In any case of severe scouring where salmonellosis is suspected veterinary advice should be sought immediately. Strict personal hygiene is necessary to minimise the risk of human infection and to limit the spread among calves. If salmonellosis is a recurring problem routine vaccination of calves may be necessary.

Pneumonia

The most common calfhood disease is pneumonia, called enzootic pneumonia because of the large number of organisms which may contribute to infection. It can be a problem in hot, sultry summer weather but is most common during periods of still, damp weather in winter. It is aggravated in stuffy buildings with poor ventilation or when the atmosphere is laden with dust from mouldy hay or straw or dusty feeds.

Pneumonia is likely to strike first mid-way through the milk feeding period and again just after weaning, especially if calves are moved to different accommodation when weather conditions are unfavourable. Whenever weather conditions are adverse a watchful eye needs to be kept on calves of all ages for any sign of infection.

At first the calf may be no more than uncomfortable, tired or hanging back at feeding time. Soon there is a nasal discharge and the calf develops runny eyes. By the time the calf starts coughing and gasping for breath with a high temperature it is dangerously at risk.

The normal veterinary treatment is a course of antibiotic injections over three or four days. If treated at an early stage of infection, calves recover quickly. Survivors of severe infection never thrive and are always susceptible to a further fatal infection.

There has been a major research effort to develop vaccines which would give some protection against enzootic pneumonia but these are not yet available commercially.

Infectious bovine rhinotracheitis (IBR) should be differentiated from other pneumonias because it is an infection of the upper respiratory tract. However, it may predispose cattle to secondary infection with bacteria which do cause pneumonia. IBR is rarely a problem in calf rearing. It is more common among older cattle and on problem farms vaccination may be necessary.

CALF REARING

The conventional approach to early weaning is to feed warm milk replacer from a bucket twice daily until the calves are weaned after five weeks. Expert calf rearers have found that they can get equally good results feeding milk replacer only once daily.

In addition to these bucket rearing systems teat feeding systems have been developed in which milk is fed *ad libitum* for the first part of the pre-weaning period. There are sophisticated automatic machines which mix warm milk replacer and dispense it to the calves. Much cheaper is feeding cold acidified milk held in a simple plastic container and dispensed through a teat. To enable early weaning after five weeks a gradual weaning procedure is employed in teat feeding systems.

Milk replacers

Whichever rearing system is adopted the quality of the milk replacer has important effects on calf health and performance. First and foremost it is essential that the milk replacer stimulates normal reflex closure of the oesophageal groove so that the liquid is carried past the forestomachs into the abomasum. It is also desirable that in the abomasum normal clotting of milk proteins should occur under the action of the enzyme rennet. This may be impaired if the milk proteins have been heated excessively during drying and calves fed these damaged proteins may scour. All milk replacers need to be fortified with vitamins A, D and E and minerals, especially magnesium.

The best milk replacers are based on dried skim milk usually supplemented with fat to bring the fat level up to 20 per cent of the dry matter. Special formulations are needed for automatic machines and the milk replacers for cold feeding contain various organic acids which ensure that the milk stays fresh for three or four days without going sour.

EEC support policies have now flattened the skim milk mountain with the result that prices have increased sharply. Attention has therefore switched to so-called 'zero' milk replacers based on cheaper dried whey, often supplemented with non-milk proteins and amino acids. On the best of these, calf performance is not far short of skim milk replacers and the cost is 25 per cent less.

There is interest in the use of probiotics as a possible means of improving performance in the milk-fed calf. Several commercial products are available, usually cultures of *Lactobacilli*, *Bacillus subtilis* or *Streptococcus faecium*, which are normal inhabitants of the gut. They are claimed to be beneficial by improving the gut flora, so inhibiting the growth of pathogens.

Whilst the probiotic concept is sound, trial results are very variable and more work is needed to identify effective products and define the conditions under which probiotics bring consistent improvements in performance.

Bucket rearing

For bucket rearing, calves are best housed in individual pens. However, for calves housed in groups some rearers use a bank of narrow calf crates in which calves are held while milk replacer is being fed. One set of crates can serve several groups of calves.

The first job is to teach calves to drink from a bucket which usually presents few problems. The calf is allowed to suck two fingers which have been dipped into the milk replacer and then the calf's mouth is guided down into the milk. With the most perverse calves a nipple feeder usually does the trick. For the best hygiene each calf should have its own milk bucket.

For anyone other than an expert calf rearer, twice daily bucket feeding is the system of choice because it involves regular inspection of the calves. The milk powder is mixed at 125 g per litre of warm water, aiming at a temperature of the liquid in front of the calf at 38–40°C.

The first feed of milk replacer on the second morning should be 1 litre and then the level is built up steadily over 7–10 days to 2 litres per feed. If there is slight scouring cut back the milk replacer and if scouring is more severe stop feeding and give an electrolyte solution. Over the five-week period about 16 kg of milk powder is used.

Fresh concentrates containing 18 per cent crude protein with a good UDP rating and clean drinking water should be available throughout the pre-weaning period. Proprietary early weaning concentrates are usually pelleted but some companies produce attractive coarse mixes. Home mixes with 18 per cent crude protein should always include some fishmeal as a source of UDP and should contain at least 12.5 MJ ME per kg DM; performance is improved by an in-feed growth promoter such as Romensin (Elanco) or Avotan (Cyanamid) (Table 9.1).

Calves are weaned at 35 days provided they are eating at least 1 kg of concentrate daily, otherwise milk replacer is fed for a few days longer.

Pens should be bedded regularly with clean barley straw so that calves can eat some as an aid to normal rumination. This is better than feeding hay which the calves like but which depresses concentrate intake and calf performance.

Table 9.1 Example of home mixed early weaning concentrate.

	% by weight
Rolled barley	50.0
Flaked maize	25.0
White fishmeal	8.0
Extracted soya bean meal	10.0
Molasses	5.0
Minerals/vitamins	2.0
Growth promoter	Manufacturer's recommendations

Expert rearers can reduce the frequency of feeding to once daily with a 30 per cent saving in labour but little or no loss of calf performance. Nevertheless, close inspection of the calves at other times of day is essential.

The milk replacer is mixed at 150 g per litre. On the morning of the second day the calf is fed 1 litre which is then increased gradually over 7–10 days to 2.75 litres per feed. The consumption of milk powder is about 13 kg.

Teat rearing

Teat rearing can be advantageous when calves are housed in groups in buildings unsuitable for individual pen layouts and when greater flexibility of labour use is needed than the rigid daily routine of bucket rearing. Moreover, since calves are fed milk replacer *ad libitum* for part of the pre-weaning period early calf gains are higher than for bucket rearing. Of course the better performance is achieved at the cost of higher milk input.

It is all too easy to overestimate the saving in labour of teat rearing. It probably takes longer to teach calves to drink than in bucket rearing. Equipment must still be kept scrupulously clean. And the temptation to reduce the frequency of inspection of calves must be guarded against or disease incidence increases. Indeed, disease control is more difficult because, with several calves sharing the same teat and physical contact in group housing, infection spreads more than among calves penned individually.

Nonetheless, teat rearing does give greater flexibility of labour use because, apart from routine inspection of the calves, jobs can be done when it is convenient during the day.

Automatic machines are usually fitted with four teats and at 10 calves per teat, which is ideal, can service four pens arranged round the machine, each containing 10 calves. The calves can be of different age groups which is convenient for homebred calves or where small numbers are purchased at a time.

When they have settled in calves are taken to the teat and trained to suckle which is normally accomplished in a single lesson lasting a few minutes. Shy feeders may need taking to the teat for a few days until they are observed suckling normally.

The machine is usually set to reconstitute milk replacer at 125 g per litre. Milk intake builds up much more quickly than in bucket feeding and the faeces are quite loose. This is normal but if scouring becomes established affected calves should be penned away from the machine and fed an electrolyte solution.

To allow weaning after five weeks gradual weaning needs to be started after three weeks. This is achieved through shutting off the milk supply by removing the teats at first overnight and then progressively longer each day. It helps to stimulate concentrate consumption if the trough is put in place of the teats. Total milk replacer consumption in the five-week period is 25–30 kg, considerably higher than for bucket rearing.

Concentrate consumption is low early on but a supply should be made available right from the start. Consumption is lower at weaning than for bucket-reared calves but after a brief check consumption soon increases. Fresh drinking water should be available throughout.

Automatic machines are expensive and so some calf rearers have preferred the cold acidified milk system of rearing. Because cold acidified milk replacer stays fresh for three days or so it only needs to be mixed two or three times a week and can be stored in an inexpensive plastic dustbin. The milk replacer is mixed with cold water (minimum 10°C) at 125 g per litre and is drawn to the teats through plastic tubes fitted with non-return valves.

Management of the calves is the same as for automatic machines except that six calves per teat is preferable because the calves may drink cold milk more slowly than warm milk; it is simple enough to provide an extra teat if it is needed.

There is a suggestion, not supported conclusively by research, that calves fed acidified milk suffer less scouring than those fed non-acidified replacers.

During very cold weather the intake of milk replacer may be subnormal and in this situation it is advisable to use an immersion heater to take the chill off the liquid.

Post-weaning

As indicated earlier the immediate post-weaning period is a time to watch out for pneumonia, especially if calves have been moved to different accommodation and weather conditions are unfavourable.

For the first three weeks post-weaning the early weaning concentrate should continue to be fed *ad libitum*. The specialist rearer selling calves at three months is aiming at a high three-month weight and will feed concentrates *ad libitum* throughout. However, after eight weeks there is a strong case for preparing calves gradually for their later rearing system.

For example, calves destined for cereal beef should start being fed the cereal/protein mix with the early weaning concentrate. The proportion of cereal/protein mix is increased gradually so that there is not a sudden change of diet at three months.

A gradual transition of diet is even more important for calves going into forage systems. After eight weeks they can start being fed hay or silage with the early weaning concentrate rationed at $2\frac{1}{2}$ kg daily. It is very important that the hay or silage is of very high quality. Even then the introduction of forage will reduce current gain slightly, but it ensures a smooth transition to a high-forage diet with longer-term advantages. Also, feed costs during the rearing period are reduced.

Calf rearing targets

Targets for calf rearing which should be achieved with careful management are shown in Table 9.2. These targets are for calves fed concentrates *ad libitum* to three months but if forage is fed in the last month reared weights would be about 10 kg lower and concentrate input about 30 kg lower.

The startling difference in calf performance between calf rearing units with good financial results and those with poor results is ably demonstrated by MLC records (Table 9.3). Top third units combined very low calf mortality with high daily gains pre- and post-weaning. By contrast bottom third units had a crippling level of calf mortality and lower than average pre-weaning gains, caused presumably by a high incidence of calfhood diseases.

VEAL PRODUCTION

The British veal industry is tiny and contracting but in continental EEC countries veal is a major industry and accounts for around 8 million calves annually. The major producers are France, Italy, the Netherlands, Spain and West Germany.

The calves are fed milk replacer *ad libitum* and the trend is to longer

Table 9.2 Calf rearing targets.

| | Friesian/Holstein(F), Hereford × F, Limousin × F, Belgian Blue × F | | | Charolais × F, Simmental × F | | |
| | Bucket rearing | | Teat rearing | Bucket rearing | | Teat rearing |
	2 × daily	1 × daily		2 × daily	1 × daily	
Feeds (kg)						
– milk replacer	16	13	25–30	16	13	25–30
– concentrates	175	180	165	185	190	175
Calf mortality (%)	<3	<3	<3	<3	<3	<3
Daily gain (kg)						
– pre-weaning	0.5	0.4	0.7	0.5	0.4	0.7
– post-weaning	1.0	1.0	0.9	1.1	1.1	1.0
Reared calf at 3 months (kg)	115	110	120	125	120	130

Table 9.3 Performance results from commercial calf units, 1987.
(Source: *MLC Beef Yearbook, 1988.*)

	Bottom third	Average gross margin per calf	Top third
Feeds (kg)			
– milk replacer	13	14	14
– concentrates	170	165	160
Calf mortality (%)	9	4	<1
Daily gain (kg)			
– pre-weaning	0.50	0.53	0.76
– post-weaning	0.89	0.94	0.90
Reared calf (kg)	108	116	123

feeding periods and a higher carcase weight. In the Netherlands, for example, which has led this trend the average carcase weight has increased by 40 kg during the 1980s to 150 kg in 1987. Typically calves are fed for 22 weeks to a liveweight of 220 kg.

Veal production is particularly suitable for extreme dairy Friesian/Holstein calves which produce a more acceptable carcase than they do in beef systems.

In recent years veal has come under pressure as a product. There have been incidents of illegal use of banned growth promoting hormones which have undermined consumer confidence in the wholesomeness of veal. There is also welfare concern about the practice of rearing veal calves in narrow crates only 70 cm wide with slatted floors which prevent the calves from turning round or lying down comfortably. Feeding an all-milk diet which is deficient in iron causing anaemia and denying normal rumen function is also a matter of concern.

British welfare legislation is being enacted which would ban veal crates. Also, it would require that the available iron content of milk replacers should be declared and that from two weeks of age calves should have access to dry food containing digestible fibre to stimulate functional rumen development. EEC legislation is bound to follow this British lead.

Initiatives for better calf welfare have already been taken by producers with the development of group housing systems. But as soon as concentrates are fed veal loses its anaemic 'white' appearance and it remains to be seen how 'pink' veal will fare in the market place.

Added to these consumer issues, the economic viability of veal production is threatened by the high cost of calves as dairy cow numbers decline. Also, there has been a sharp increase in the price of milk replacers because dried skim milk is no longer in surplus. This is important because over the 22-week feeding period calves consume 285 kg of milk powder.

10 Dairy Beef Production

The range of available dairy beef systems can accommodate calves born at any time of year and is flexible enough to be adapted to individual farm circumstances. The higher the lifetime average daily gain the earlier is the slaughter date and the lighter the slaughter weight.

It is in the development of dairy beef systems that the concept of planned production has made most progress, especially where the whole production process takes place on a single farm (see also Chapter 5).

Systems include: cereal beef in which cattle are fed an all-concentrate diet and slaughtered at 11–13 months of age; grass silage beef in which a silage/cereal ration is fed to cattle slaughtered at 14–17 months; maize silage beef with slaughter at 12–16 months; 18-month beef where autumn-born calves are grazed during their first summer and finished the following winter on silage/cereal at 16–20 months; and grass beef with grass finishing at 20–24 months of age following a store winter. There is also a good deal of trading in dairy-bred stores which drop out from one system or another or are reared without a particular system in mind.

Cereal beef and grass silage beef have year-round production capability. Also, because cattle are housed throughout, these systems lend themselves to bull beef.

BULL BEEF

Some of the considerations involved in bull beef were discussed in Chapter 6. The attraction of bull beef is the faster, leaner and more efficient growth than steers. Also, the market pays premiums for bull beef.

Bull beef must always be an option in housed beef systems provided buildings are suitable for bulls or can be adapted at reasonable cost. Bull beef is less attractive in systems involving grazing because in Britain the safety code for grazing bulls over 10 months of age stipulates standards of boundary fencing which are far too expensive to be practicable.

Safe handling is a major consideration in establishing a bull beef unit. The management of bulls presents no insuperable problems but their behaviour is more determined and the occasional bull becomes aggressive. Therefore as much of the daily routine as possible, especially feeding and bedding, should be possible from outside the pen. If it becomes necessary to enter a pen the stockworker should carry a stick and a lookout should be posted outside the pen.

There is a huge market for bull beef in continental Europe and, although the trade has been slow to accept bulls in Britain, there is now no shortage of outlets, both through live auctions and deadweight sales. Inevitably there has been an expansion of bull beef production in Britain since the EEC ban on hormone implants.

It cannot be stressed too often how important it is to handle bulls quietly during marketing right through from farm to slaughter point, to minimise the risk of stress-induced dark cutting beef (see Chapter 2). This is especially important during the winter months when the incidence of dark cutting is at its peak.

CEREAL BEEF

Cereal beef, known to most farmers as barley beef, was developed originally during the 1950s by Dr T.R. Preston working at the Rowett Research Institute. Barley beef has the highest average daily gain of any dairy beef system. It is sometimes called intensive beef which is misleading because grass-based systems can also be intensive.

Dairy-bred cattle, almost invariably bulls, are fed an all-concentrate diet *ad libitum* and grow rapidly to reach slaughter at 11–13 months of age, depending on breed/cross.

Because the cattle are housed throughout, year-round production is possible and indeed is encouraged by buyers who pay a premium for level supply. The enterprise makes no direct use of land and so can be added to an arable or dairy farm provided suitable buildings and the necessary cattle management skills are available.

Profitability is sensitive to relationships between the purchase price of calves, concentrate costs and the sale value of slaughter cattle. In the early 1960s calves and barley were cheap in relation to sale values and the system was so widely adopted in Britain that it may have accounted for 15 per cent of home-produced beef. Since then profitability has been lower in real terms and rather variable from year to year with the result that barley beef now accounts for no more than five per cent of home-produced beef. Nevertheless, barley beef is long-established and supplies a special market which pays a premium.

Management

Reared calves three months old are fed *ad libitum* a rolled barley/protein mix with a crude protein content of 14 per cent. Ideally this concentrate should have been introduced gradually during the last month of the calf rearing period.

Proprietary protein/vitamin/mineral supplements contain about 35 per cent crude protein and the convention is to mix 85 per cent rolled barley with 15 per cent protein premix to achieve 14 per cent crude protein overall. However, the variation in the crude protein content of barley is sufficient to make a feed analysis of the barley worthwhile so that the mix can be adjusted more precisely.

If the protein supplement is home-mixed it is important that it has a high UDP rating to meet the needs of rapidly growing cattle through to six months of age. Vitamin and mineral levels are also important, especially of vitamin A which has a high requirement in the system.

Proprietary protein supplements usually contain an in-feed growth promoter such as monensin sodium (Romensin, Elanco) or avotan (Cyanamid). These modify rumen fermentation to cut down methane loss and increase the ratio of desirable propionic acid in the mix of volatile fatty acids. The result is an improvement in feed conversion efficiency, though not necessarily an increase in growth rate.

UK regulations require farmers incorporating in-feed growth promoters or other medications into home-mixed concentrates to register with the Pharmaceutical Society of Great Britain and follow approved procedures.

Barley should be rolled so that the grain is squashed flat but not shattered to produce a dusty feed which may exacerbate respiratory disease. Careful rolling also helps to reduce the incidence of bloat and acidosis. Rolling is easiest if moist grain can be used.

In some situations where a small barley beef unit is established on a farm without rolling equipment it may be financially advantageous to purchase a compound concentrate rather than install a mill. This would only be the case where the compound can be delivered and stored in bulk because bagged feed is so much more expensive.

Wheat has an even higher value than barley and at a cost up to 5 per cent more per tonne can replace part of the barley. Usually not more than 50 per cent of rolled wheat would be included to avoid possible digestive upsets from a low fibre diet.

Dried molassed sugar beet pulp has a slightly lower ME value than barley and can replace up to 30 per cent of the cereal. The problem with beet pulp is that it tends to separate out of the concentrate mix in the hopper.

There has been some interest in supplementing the cereal with protected fat to sustain energy intake through the final stages of finishing when otherwise daily gains tail off. Trial results with 2.5 per cent of protected fat added to the cereal show a small increase in daily gain, reduced feed intake and improved feed conversion efficiency. At present prices for protected fat financial margins are improved by including it in the ration.

At six months of age the usual recommendation is to reduce the protein supplement from 15 to 10 per cent so that the overall crude protein is 12 per cent. At the same time it is possible to switch to a cheaper protein supplement in which urea is used to replace part of the protein. The daily intake of urea should be held at no more than 100 g and in practice proprietary protein supplements rarely contain more than 4 per cent of urea.

On occasions dried poultry manure has been used to replace part or all of the protein in the cheaper mix fed from six months. The trouble is that it reduces the energy value of the whole ration and is likely to reduce daily gains. Under normal price relationships it would not come into the reckoning.

The rate of lean meat gain in continental breed × Friesian bulls is so high that there is a strong argument for maintaining the crude protein content of the overall ration at 14 per cent right through to slaughter. Nevertheless a cheaper protein premix can be used from six months.

The concentrate mix is usually fed from a bulk hopper and the protein supplement is either mixed with the rolled barley before the hoppers are filled or spread on top of the barley so that it mixes as feed passes down through the hopper.

For bulls there should be not more than 20 cattle per pen with a hopper providing at least 75 mm trough space per bull, preferably 100 mm. The hopper should be located near the front of the pen so that it can be inspected frequently and safely, removing soiled feed and making sure that there is an even flow of concentrate mix into the trough.

Any interruption to feeding because the hopper runs out, the concentrate mix bridges in the hopper or the water supply fails runs the risk of acidosis because cattle gorge themselves when they start feeding again. The rumen wall becomes inflamed, the blood is acid and dehydration sets in. The cattle may recover after a day or so or the symptoms may progress to collapse and death. Prompt veterinary advice should be sought if acidosis is suspected.

Mild acidosis is always possible in barley beef units and is associated with the liver abscesses which cause a significant number of damaged livers to be condemned at the meat plant. If the rumen wall is inflamed it is susceptible to penetration by sharp objects such as barley awns, hairs or sharp stones.

The damage opens the way for bacteria to cause ruminitis, seen as clumping of the rumen villi. These bacteria then enter the blood stream and pass to the liver where they cause abscesses. Because the liver is so large there is not usually a noticeable effect on performance and the condition is not revealed until the cattle are slaughtered.

Against this background trials have been carried out to study the effects of including sodium bicarbonate in barley beef concentrates as a rumen buffer. By reducing acidity in the rumen it could be expected to improve the utilisation of nutrients. Recent trials in which 2 per cent of sodium bicarbonate has been added to barley beef diets have shown a 5 per cent improvement in daily gains and feed conversion efficiency.

Bloat is an ever-present problem with all-concentrate diets but its incidence is limited if cattle are able to eat about 1 kg per day of barley straw. They pick this up from the bedding if cattle are bedded daily but on slatted floors straw should be fed from racks. Straw intake is insufficient to reduce concentrate intake and growth rate.

Steers and heifers are not well suited to barley beef because they fatten at excessively light weights. For the same reason Hereford × Friesians and other early maturing crosses are not suitable either; they are far better exploited in forage-based beef systems.

Late maturing crosses are best suited to the system because they can be

Table 10.1 Targets for cereal (barley) beef from three months of age.

	Friesian/Holstein	Belgian Blue/ Limousin × Friesian	Charolais/Simmental × Friesian
Reared calf (kg)	110	110	120
Daily gain (kg)	1.3	1.3	1.4
Concentrate (tonnes)	1.8	1.9	2.0
Feed conversion (kg feed/kg gain)	5.2	4.9	5.0
Slaughter age (months)	11.5	12.5	12.5
Slaughter weight (kg)	460	490	520
Carcase weight (kg)	250	280	290
Main carcase class (EUROP)	O+3	–U3*	–U3

* Belgian Blue × Friesian U+3

Table 10.2 Profile of performance for Friesian/Holstein bulls in cereal beef.

	Daily gain (kg)	Daily feed (kg)	kg feed per kg gain
3–6 months	1.3	5.4	4.2
6–9 months	1.4	7.3	5.2
9–11½ months	1.3	8.4	6.5
Overall	1.3	6.8	5.2

taken to high slaughter weights without becoming over fat. Friesian/ Holsteins are less efficient than continental breed × Friesians and produce much poorer carcases but can be fed profitably provided they can be purchases as calves £60–£65 cheaper.

Targets for cereal beef are shown in Table 10.1.

For cattle performing at the target level there is a profile of performance with gains and feed conversion efficiency at their best in the period 6–9 months of age, worsening as the cattle approach slaughter (Table 10.2).

Achieving the daily gain targets is the key to good profitability. This is demonstrated by MLC Beefplan results from commercial barley beef units which show that the high daily gains of top third units reduced the duration of the feeding period and improved feed conversion efficiency (Table 10.3).

It is much easier to achieve high daily gains in summer when they are at least 10 per cent higher than in winter. Part of the explanation is probably that clinical and subclinical respiratory disease drag down performance in

Table 10.3 MLC Beefplan results from commercial cereal beef units, 1987. (Source: *MLC Beef Yearbook*, 1988.)

	Bottom third	Average gross margin per head	Top third
Gross margin per head (£)	22	75	123
Feeding period (days)	376	371	364
Mortality (%)	6	5	4
Calf weight (kg)	51	50	49
Daily gain from 12 weeks (kg)	1.14	1.18	1.23
Concentrates from 12 weeks (kg)	1976	1825	1653
kg feed per kg gain	5.8	5.3	4.7
Slaughter weight (kg)	451	457	463
Killing-out (%)	54	55	55
Carcase weight (kg)	245	249	253

the winter months, even when cattle are housed in airy but daught-free buildings.

Marketing

Most barley beef is marketed deadweight and year-round producers are often able to negotiate level supply premiums with buyers. With its characteristic marble-white fat, barley beef commands a small premium in its specialist market. The premium rises to a peak in the autumn as buyers safeguard supplies when beef prices are at their seasonal low. In the last few years several auction markets have begun to sell bulls and have realised considerable premiums over the equivalent steer price.

Over the years buyers have increased their preferred carcase weight, largely to accommodate high quality continental breed × Friesians. However, there is usually a drop in price for carcases above a threshold weight set somewhere in the range 310–320 kg.

Bull beef carcases are mainly in EEC fat class 3 with a few in 4L. These are all paid at the same price per kg though some buyers discriminate against ultra-lean carcases in fat classes 1 and 2, especially if they are of poor conformation. Indeed, poor conformation is penalised heavily with a sharp drop in price for –O and P conformation carcases from the poorest Friesian/Holsteins. Too many buying schedules lump –U and better conformation carcases together at the same price which leaves the best conformation cattle, e.g. Belgian Blue × Friesian short of the price they need to recoup the high calf cost.

An interpretation of the discussion on marketing strategies in Chapter 8 is that slow growers within a pen should be slaughtered as soon as they get into the buyer's preferred weight range, unless they are on the verge of a higher price grade. Fast growers can be retained until they get to the upper end of the preferred weight range provided they do not slip into an overfat class. The faster the average daily gain of the pen, the more efficiently is feed utilised and the higher will be the most profitable slaughter weight within the buyer's preferred weight range.

GRASS SILAGE BEEF

Grass silage beef was derived from the 18-month beef system during the late 1970s and has been adopted on many farms for three main reasons:

(1) It avoids the complications of grazing cattle.

(2) Stocking rates can be much higher than in an integrated grazing/ conservation beef system.
(3) Bull beef can be produced year-round from a forage-based system.

Grass silage beef is sometimes called storage beef which is a term not at all clear in its meaning and is therefore best avoided.

Many producers have switched into grass silage beef from 18-month beef and have been surprised that stocking rates are more than doubled. So if the same area of grassland is retained there is a massive increase in the working capital needed to fund production. Also there is usually a need for additional silage clamps to accommodate the extra silage needed and to provide a separate clamp for summer feeding. On the other hand, year-round production makes more efficient use of calf rearing facilities and cattle buildings and there is not necessarily a need for new building investment. Also, once the system is established, the cash flow is much more even than for a seasonal system such as 18-month beef.

Most producers use bulls but in some situations steers are reared and there is a place for heifers in the system. Slaughter is in the age range 13–17 months, depending on breed and sex. However, there is considerable scope for manipulating the ratio of cereal to silage in the ration to adjust growth rate, slaughter age and slaughter weight.

High quality silage is vital to the success of the system with at least 10.5 MJ ME per kg DM the aim. With poor quality silage there is a loss of flexibility in ration design and excessive levels of concentrates are necessary to support target gains. The required silage quality can be achieved in a four-cut regime with an early first cut and regrowths cut every five or six weeks. Producers aiming at ultra-high silage quality may cut five times during the season.

Frequent cutting for silage implies intensive grassland management and top producers fertilise grass swards with 350–400 kg N per hectare. At this level of intensity grass/clover swards with no N fertiliser input are not a realistic alternative because of the substantially reduced stocking rate. Also, the management of grass/clover swards is not easy under continuous cutting and the herbage is more difficult to make into a silage with good fermentation characteristics than grass.

Attention to detail during silage making is essential to produce a well-fermented silage which cattle eat with relish.

Management

Ideally, calves should be introduced to silage during the last month of the rearing period so that at three months they make a smooth transition to the silage diet.

From three to six months silage is fed to appetite with concentrates rationed to achieve a daily gain of 1.0 kg. At this stage there is a clear-cut daily gain response of about 0.1 kg to feeding 0.4 kg daily of a protein supplement with a high UDP rating. This provides for the UDP requirement of the calf and, by balancing the high non-protein nitrogen content of the silage, stimulates an increase in silage intake. It could be argued that with the highest quality silage this is the only concentrate supplement required. However, producers take a more cautious view and generally also feed $1\frac{1}{2}$–2 kg mineralised rolled barley.

At six months the protein can be withdrawn and the silage supplemented with 2–$2\frac{1}{2}$ kg of mineralised rolled barley or other cereal to achieve a daily gain of 1.0–1.1 kg in bulls. If possible the daily intake of silage should be recorded periodically and if it is below the calculated ration the cereal level increased to restore daily gain to the target level. Waiting until the cattle are weighed to find out that gains are below target risks losing so much time that the shortfall cannot be clawed back.

The precise daily gain response to additional cereal depends on the extent to which it substitutes for silage intake. To sustain the target gain it is probably necessary gradually to increase cereal feeding to 3 kg per day at 12 months of age, perhaps 4 kg for Charolais × Friesian bulls of high growth potential.

Even higher levels of concentrates may be fed, if silage is in short supply, to increase daily gain and bring forward the slaughter date, with a considerable saving in silage.

An in-feed growth promoter can be supplied via the mineral mix or alternatively Romensin (Elanco) is available as a rumen bolus with a pay-out over 150 days. On forage diets there is a valuable daily gain response of 0.05–0.08 kg.

A majority of grass silage beef producers use bulls and the targets in Table 10.4 are for bull beef. It is difficult to justify steer production unless buildings are unsuitable for bulls or a buyer can be found willing to pay a substantial premium for steers. The earlier maturity of steers would be exploited either by finishing cattle earlier at a lighter weight than bulls, or by growing steers more slowly to higher slaughter weights. Heifers can also be used, particularly lean continental breed × Friesians and gross margin per hectare can rival bulls because, although gross margin per head is lower, stocking rate can be higher.

For the same reason that different sexes can be used in grass silage beef, so can the whole range of breeds and crosses. Continental breed × Friesians

Table 10.4 Targets for bulls in grass silage beef from three months of age.

	Friesian/Holstein	Hereford × Friesian	Belgian Blue/Limousin × Friesian	Charolais/Simmental × Friesian
Reared calf (kg)	110	110	110	120
Daily gain (kg)*	1.0	1.0	1.0	1.1
Protein concentrate (kg)	40	40	40	40
Cereal (tonnes)*	1.0	0.9	1.0	1.1
Silage (tonnes, 25% DM)*	6.0	5.0	6.0	6.5
Stocking (bulls per ha)	8.5	10.0	8.5	8.0
Slaughter age (months)	16	15	17	16
Slaughter weight (kg)	500	475	525	550
Carcase weight (kg)	265	255	295	305
Main carcase class (EUROP)	O+3	R3	−U3**	−U3

* From 12 weeks
** Belgian Blue × Friesian U+3

are used increasingly in grass silage beef and, provided Limousin × Friesians cost not more than £60–65 extra than Friesian/Holsteins and Charolais × Friesians £65–70, they have similar profit potential. Hereford × Friesians are worth £30–35 more than Friesian/Holsteins. Being slaughtered at a lighter weight they make a lower gross margin per head but, eating less silage, they can be stocked more heavily and make a similar gross margin per hectare.

Respiratory disease can be particularly troublesome in grass silage beef because the cattle are housed throughout. It is a risk in sultry summer weather as well as in still, damp winter conditions. In summer it helps to maintain air flow if the building can be opened up by removal of some of the space-boarding panels. It helps to reduce stocking density during the hottest summer months.

The other consequences of continuous housing are overgrown feet and cases of foul in the foot. A concrete strip on which cattle stand to feed helps to keep feet in shape. Also, ringworm is a problem on some farms.

MLC Beefplan results from commercial grass silage beef units (Table 10.5) show that producers with the top third of gross margins per hectare achieved higher daily gains than average and so were able to carry cattle to a higher slaughter weight in the same feeding period. Not immediately obvious in the results is the higher quality of silage made by top third producers which permitted higher daily gains on rations including less concentrates and no more silage than average. Moreover, at the expense of slightly higher N fertiliser use, silage yield per hectare was higher leading to

Table 10.5 MLC Beefplan results from commercial grass silage beef units, 1987. (Source: *MLC Beef Yearbook*, 1988.)

	Bottom third	Average gross margin per hectare	Top third
Gross margin per head (£)	93	133	169
Gross margin per hectare (£)	523	995	1508
Feeding period (days)	373	373	374
Reared calf (kg)	118	116	110
Daily gain (kg)	0.97	1.01	1.05
Concentrates (tonnes)	1.01	0.93	0.90
Silage (tonnes)	5.8	5.4	5.5
Silage per hectare (tonnes)	33	40	49
Stocking (cattle per ha)	5.6	7.5	8.9
N fertiliser (kgN/ha)	300	320	375
Slaughter weight (kg)	480	493	503
Carcase weight (kg)	260	268	274

a higher stocking rate of cattle. Bottom third performance was poor all round and stemmed from the inability to make a high tonnage per hectare of high quality silage.

Grass silage beef can be modified by replacing part of the silage/cereal diet by arable wastes such as surplus potatoes, carrots, etc. These can find a place if the cost is right but should not deflect attention from the main business of producing high quality silage.

There has also been interest in a complete dairy beef system using roots such as swedes or fodder beet. In the past root feeding has always been thought of as a modification of barley beef but it is better seen as an alternative to grass silage beef. The problem with roots is that whilst they are an excellent basis of a winter finishing ration, they are difficult to store during the summer months.

Marketing

Development of the grass silage beef system was production-led, that is it sprang from a desire to improve grassland utilisation and to create year-round production from a forage system. The product was not aimed at a particular market.

For a time it looked as though there would be a very limited market for bull beef from cattle slaughtered at 14–17 months of age. In the event, as grass silage beef has expanded and reliable supplies of this type of beef have become available the market has opened up well. Indeed it could be argued that a buyer seeking consistent beef supplies produced from a single forage-based feeding system would be naturally drawn to grass silage beef.

As with barley beef most producers sell deadweight. The poor conformation of Friesian/Holsteins is even more apparent at this older slaughter age. So the severe discounts for conformation class –O and P can punish returns, if as so often happens, 20–30 per cent of Friesian/Holstein carcases fall into the poor conformation zone of the classification grid.

At a daily gain of 1.0–1.1 kg the rate of fattening of bulls is very slow and it takes them two or three months to traverse a single EEC fat class. This gives a good deal of scope for modifying marketing strategies and fitting-in with different buyers' weight preferences.

Bull carcases of the late maturing Friesian/Holstein and continental beef breed × Friesians are predominantly in fat class 3 but Hereford × Friesians are fatter and a few may slip into fat class 4H which is penalised by almost all buyers. This is a bigger risk with steers and heifers which need to be handled regularly through the final stages of finishing to check fatness.

The argument for slaughtering slow growers at the first opportunity and keeping fast growers longer applies to grass silage beef. However, the slaughter strategy also needs to take account of silage stocks. If silage is short it will probably pay better to slaughter a batch of cattle slightly earlier than usual rather than have to modify the rations of all the younger batches or delay purchase of the next group of calves.

MAIZE SILAGE BEEF

Maize is one of the world's major grain crops and is probably its major arable forage crop. In continental Europe maize has spread northwards rapidly as plant breeders have developed earlier maturing varieties. However, the crop is still marginal in Britain except on favoured sites in southern and eastern areas.

Continental European beef producers in Italy, Germany and France have developed maize silage beef systems for both dairy-bred and suckler-bred cattle. Maize silage forms a greater part of the ration than in USA feedlots but is still supplemented heavily with maize grain.

One benefit of the maize crop is that it is environmentally friendly to the extent that it responds well to heavy applications of slurry or FYM. Moreover, the stover (stalks) and root system from a previous crop form a 'raft' across the field so that slurry can be applied even under fairly wet conditions.

As the crop matures after flowering, sugars formed in the leaves are transferred to the ears and stored as starch in the grain. The ear forms an increasing proportion of the crop and so, despite falling digestibility of the leaf and stem, overall digestibility stays fairly constant over a long period while yield continues to increase. In fact the crop is not cut for silage until it has quite a dry appearance when the grain is at the 'late dough' stage.

Maize is made easily into a well-fermented silage which cattle eat in large quantities. Under British conditions maize silage is usually around 25 per cent DM but in drier climates higher DM contents are achieved; below 22 per cent DM effluent production is profuse. The main worry in Britain is always whether the crop can be harvested before wet autumn weather sets in. The other cause for concern is secondary fermentation at the silage face during the summer. A narrow clamp is best with careful removal of silage to prevent the face becoming loose.

Whilst maize silage is a superb source of energy, typically with 11.2 MJ ME per kg DM, it is very short of protein. Quite often British growers feed a mixed ration of maize silage and grass silage which produces a high energy feed with adequate protein.

Table 10.6 Targets for maize silage beef.

	Friesian/Holstein	Hereford × Friesian	Limousin/Belgian Blue × Friesian	Charolais/Simmental × Friesian
Reared calf (kg)	110	110	110	120
Daily gain (kg)	1.1	1.1	1.1	1.2
Protein supplement (kg)	500	450	550	500
Maize silage (tonnes at 25% DM)	7.0	6.0	7.0	7.5
Cereal (kg)	100	0	100	100
Slaughter age (months)	14	13	15	14
Slaughter weight (kg)	475	450	500	525
Carcase weight (kg)	250	245	280	290
Main carcase class (EUROP)	O+3	R3	–U3*	–U3

* Belgian Blue × Friesian U+3

Relationships between falling protein requirements as cattle grow but increasing maize silage intake, has led to the proposal that a simple maize silage beef system could be based on flat-rate feeding of 1.5 kg daily of a 35 per cent crude protein supplement with maize silage to appetite. The protein supplement would also carry vitamins, minerals and in in-feed growth promoter. Some cereal may be needed in the last three months to sustain daily gain. There are similarities between this approach and grass silage beef.

Targets for the system are shown in Table 10.6. There are no recorded results to evaluate the performance of the system under commercial conditions.

EIGHTEEN-MONTH BEEF

Eighteen-month beef was the first planned beef system and developed from the realisation that well-grown yearling cattle at the end of the grazing season, which at that time were stored through the winter, could in fact be finished at about 18 months of age on a ration of silage or hay supplemented with cereals. There was parallel development of the system by researchers and leading dairy beef producers during the 1960s and in 1967 the first handbook for a planned beef system, 18-month beef, was published.

Looking back to that time it is depressing how many professional advisers scorned the concept of planned systems, arguing that individual farm circumstances varied too much to allow a systematic approach. Happily, attitudes are very different now.

Essentially, 18-month beef takes autumn-born calves from the main calving season of the UK dairy herd which are reared through the first winter, grazed from 6–12 months of age and finished on silage/cereal at 16–20 months of age. The range of slaughter ages indicates that there is flexibility in planning the system for the individual farm.

Management

Early weaned calves should be introduced to silage during the last month of the rearing period. Then from three months until turnout in the spring silage is fed *ad libitum* with a cereal concentrate rationed at $2\frac{1}{2}$ kg daily. From birth in the autumn to turnout in the spring the target is a daily gain of 0.8 kg. Calves are then in ideal condition for turnout to grazing weighing about 180 kg.

There is a temptation, particularly with late-born calves, to feed for higher daily gains during the rearing winter to inflate turnout weights. However, this makes the calves overfat and grazing gains are lower than for lean calves at turnout which exhibit compensatory growth.

The fact is that calves born later than October do not fit well into 18-month beef. If late-born calves have to be used they are best fed for moderate gains through the rearing winter but supplemented with concentrates throughout the grazing season to improve yarding weights. Really, these calves are better diverted to barley beef or grass silage beef.

If husk is a problem and is controlled by vaccine the vaccination programme should be carried out before turnout (see Chapter 7).

At turnout to grazing the calves should be stocked heavily at 2500 kg liveweight per hectare which is 14 calves weighing 180 kg. A third of the overall grassland area should be available for grazing with about a quarter of it split off as a buffer grazing area (see Chapter 7).

It is not necessary to subdivide the grazed area into paddocks. Set stocking produces equally good results provided a third of the area is fertilised every 10 days with 75 kg N per hectare. There are no problems applying fertiliser while the cattle are present.

For the first two or three weeks the calves should be supplemented with $1\frac{1}{2}$ kg concentrates daily to assist the transition to grazing. The supplement is particularly important if the weather turns wet or cold.

The aim of grazing management is a daily gain of at least 0.8 kg. This can be achieved by controlling sward height at 6–8 cm until mid-season. If sward heights are in danger of falling below 6 cm the buffer area should be strip grazed using an electric fence to give sward height on the main grazing area a chance to recover. If necessary the whole of the buffer area is grazed.

At the time of first-cut silage, cut whatever part of the buffer is not needed for grazing, hopefully all of it. The aftermath is then available for grazing in mid-season, together with part of the aftermath on the main conservation area. By this time stocking should be about 2000 kg liveweight per hectare.

From mid-season grazed sward heights can be allowed to creep up to 7–10 cm because the danger of seed heading is less. If possible half the grassland area should be available for second-cut silage. Then late in the season there may be scope for a small third cut of silage, but if necessary the whole area should be grazed with a stocking rate of 1500 kg liveweight per hectare.

This would be the normal situation in a season of average rainfall on grassland fertilised at 250 kg N per hectare. The possibility of using grass/clover swards with no N fertiliser input is discussed later.

Expansion of the grazing area is necessary, partly because the cattle are growing heavier, and partly because of the decline from mid-season of herbage availability and quality and infestation with parasitic worms.

Integration of grazing and conservation helps by making fresh, clean aftermath grazing available in mid-season on the first-cut silage area. The advantage of a three-cut regime is that a succession of fresh aftermaths become available just when they are needed most.

If the worm control programme involves a mid-season dosing (see Chapter 7) the time to give it is just before the move to aftermath grazing in mid-July.

By late August the seasonal decline in herbage availability and quality has reached the point where supplementary feeding with concentrates should be resumed. Any loss of performance at this stage damages overall grazing gains and increases winter feed costs.

Grassland management through the summer has been discussed from the standpoint of grazing management to emphasise that grazing requirements should receive priority. Nevertheless, it is also very important to make sufficient silage for winter feeding and that it should be of high quality with 10.0–10.5 MJ ME per kg DM.

First cuts should be taken early when the digestibility of grass is in the 63–67D range, just as the flower heads begin to emerge. Over much of England and Wales this means cutting in mid-May, before the end of May even in late districts. The advantages of early cutting are first cut silage of high quality, quick recovery of the sward and early availability of aftermaths for grazing. Second and third cuts should be taken from regrowths no older than five or six weeks.

At yarding in the autumn yearling cattle should weigh at least 350 kg. Silage is fed to appetite and the level of cereal supplementation built up gradually over a fortnight to the required level, typically 2–2½ kg per day. An in-feed growth promoter increases daily gain by 0.05–0.08 kg per day.

There is considerable flexibility in ration design to take account of breed, sex and the amount of silage available. The aim should always be to maximise silage in the ration.

However, after a long dry season the cost of giving grazing first priority in grassland management may be a shortage of silage. Then the trick is to increase the daily cereal allowance which increases daily gain even though silage intake is depressed by the substitution effect. The higher daily gain accelerates the rate of finishing so that cattle can be slaughtered earlier, albeit at a lighter weight. The net effect is a considerable saving in silage because of the shorter feeding period but not much change in the total amount of cereal required.

The effects of ration design on daily gain, duration of the finishing period and total feed requirements are illustrated in Table 10.7 for late maturing Friesian/Holsteins and early maturing Hereford × Friesians. The analysis

Table 10.7 Winter finishing strategies for 18-month beef.

	Friesian/Holstein			Hereford × Friesian	
Daily feed (kg)					
Cereal	2.0	2.5	3.0	2.0	2.5
Silage (10.5 ME, 25% DM)	23	22	21	23	22
Performance					
Yarding weight (kg)	350	350	350	350	350
Daily gain (kg)	0.7	0.8	0.9	0.7	0.8
Finishing period (days)	285	220	165	215	150
Slaughter weight (kg)	550	525	500	500	475
Feed budget					
Cereal (kg)	570	550	495	430	375
Silage (tonnes)	6.5	4.8	3.5	4.9	3.3

emphasises the importance when designing rations of working out a feed budget to ensure that the required quantity of silage is in store. It also emphasises the importance of reviewing performance periodically during the winter to ensure that the required daily gain is being achieved.

The other source of flexibility arises from the fact that cattle remain within a single fat class for two or three months during which slaughter weight can be varied within a range of 50–75 kg.

Steers and heifers can both be utilised in 18-month beef. Steers achieve the highest gross margin per head but heifers can be stocked more heavily and can rival steers in gross margin per hectare provided heifer calves can be purchased at least £60 cheaper than bull calves.

Bulls are not suitable for 18-month beef because the British safety code requires very high standards of field fencing for bulls over 10 months of age. These are prohibitively expensive. Also there are restrictions on grazing bulls in fields crossed by public footpaths.

One possible approach which has been demonstrated at the National Agricultural Centre is to house bulls early before they reach 10 months of age. There were no insuperable grazing management problems. The bulls were finished during the winter on silage/cereals at a daily gain of 1.0–1.1 kg.

As in grass silage beef the whole range of dairy breeds and crosses can be utilised in 18-month beef. Late maturing Friesian/Holstein and continental breed × Friesians have a longer finishing winter than early maturing Hereford × Friesians. This increases the silage requirement, reducing the overall stocking rate and shifting the balance between grazing and conservation to some extent.

Targets for 18-month beef are presented in Table 10.8.

Table 10.8 Targets for 18-month beef from three months of age.

	Holstein/Friesian	Hereford × Friesian	Limousin/Belgian Blue × Friesian	Charolais/Simmental × Friesian
Reared calf (kg)	110	110	110	120
Daily gain (kg):				
– rearing winter	0.8	0.8	0.8	0.8
– grazing	0.8	0.8	0.8	0.9
– finishing winter	0.9	0.9	0.9	0.9
– overall	0.85	0.85	0.85	0.9
Cereal (tonnes)	1.0	0.9	1.1	1.2
Silage (tonnes, 25% DM)	5.5	5.0	5.5	6.0
Stocking (cattle/ha)	3.5	4.0	3.5	3.3
Slaughter age (months)	18	17	19	19
Slaughter weight (kg)	500	475	525	550
Carcase weight (kg)	265	255	295	300
Main carcase class (EUROP)	O+4L	R4L	–U3*	–U4L

* Belgian Blue × Friesian + U3

Table 10.9 MLC Beefplan results from commercial 18-month beef units, 1988. (Source: *MLC Beef Yearbook*, 1988.)

	Bottom third	Average gross margin per hectare	Top third
Gross margin per head (£)	121	199	238
Gross margin per ha (£)	381	765	988
Feeding period (days)	527	556	560
Purchased calf (kg)	48	47	47
Daily gain (kg)			
– rearing	0.69	0.71	0.75
– grazing	0.71	0.72	0.75
– finishing	0.80	0.86	0.92
– overall	0.77	0.76	0.80
Concentrates (kg)			
– rearing	435	328	310
– grazing	50	48	53
– finishing	550	473	450
– overall	1035	849	813
Silage (tonnes)	4.5	4.8	5.8
Stocking (cattle per ha)	3.2	3.9	4.2
N fertiliser (kg N per ha)	220	227	230
Slaughter weight (kg)	460	470	495

MLC Beefplan results from commercial farms (Table 10.9) show that producers with the top third of gross margins per hectare achieved higher daily gains than average both in the first and finishing winters, though grazing gains were disappointing. Top third producers used more silage than average but had a lower dependence on concentrates. And their whole enterprise was stocked more heavily than average.

Grass/clover swards

There has been renewed interest in recent years in the possibility of using grass/clover swards in place of grass swards receiving N fertiliser. The idea is relevant at a time when there is political support for more extensive production methods and growing concern about the environment. In addition, grass/clover swards are the obvious route to organic production methods.

At the outset it needs to be stressed that grass/clover is not an easy option. Grass/clover swards are more difficult to establish than grass swards, production can be disappointing in the first year or two, cattle are more

Table 10.10 Specimen costing for 18-month beef using grass/clover.

	MLC Beefplan average 1988*	Specimen costing grass/clover
Physical		
Feeding period (months)	18	18
Daily gain (kg)	0.8	0.8
Concentrates (kg)	849	849
Silage (tonnes)	4.8	4.8
Stocking (cattle per ha)	3.85	3.20
N fertiliser (kg N per ha)	227	0
Slaughter weight (kg)	470	470
Financial		
Output (£ per head)	402	402
Variable costs (£ per head)		
– milk replacer	16	16
– concentrates	106	106
– forage	36	20
– other feeds	3	3
– veterinary	12	12
– bedding	16	16
– other costs	14	14
Total variable costs	203	187
Gross margin per head (£)	199	215
Gross margin per ha (£)	765	688
Working capital per ha (£)	853	683
Bank interest @ 15% per annum	192	153
Gross margin after bank interest (£ per ha)	573	535

* Source: *MLC Beef Yearbook*, 1988.

susceptible to bloat and management is more difficult. Expert advice should be sought before making the change.

If good grass/clover swards can be established and maintained as long leys they have a place in 18-month beef. Although stocking rate is lower than for a fertilised grass sward, so are variable costs and working capital investment which means lower bank interest charges. The specimen costing in Table 10.10 suggests that the gross margin per hectare after interest charges for grass/clover can come close to grass swards.

Marketing

Cattle from the 18-month beef system are marketed in spring and early summer. So, although steer and heifer carcases from the system are very acceptable to the meat trade, the individual producer markets cattle for three or four months at most and cannot establish the consistent relationship with a buyer enjoyed by, say, a year-round grass silage beef producer.

There is the usual problem of low prices for Holstein/Friesians of –O or worse conformation. More important is the danger of cattle slipping into overfat class 4H. Particular care needs to be taken with early maturing Hereford × Friesians and heifers of all breed types.

The policy of slaughtering slow-growing cattle early and retaining fast growers until they reach the upper end of the acceptable weight range applies to 18-month beef. However, tactics need to take account of silage stocks. If these are plentiful it may be advantageous to feed cattle to higher slaughter weights rather than carrying silage stocks forward into the next year.

GRASS BEEF

Grass beef has the longest production cycle of all the dairy beef systems and for this reason is rarely practised in its entirety on a single farm. Many of the dairy-bred stores traded through auction markets are sold at intermediate stages of this type of production.

Autumn- and winter-born calves are reared through the first winter, grazed and then fed a store ration through the second winter in preparation for grass finishing at 20–24 months of age. Cattle which fail to finish off grass are usually yarded for winter finishing.

Management

Calves born in the autumn and through to mid-winter are suitable for the system. They are early weaned and fed through the rearing winter the same as for 18-month beef.

Grassland management has to contend with two age groups of calves, the calves and grass finishing cattle a year older. The best total performance is achieved when the grazing management of the two age groups is integrated. The leader/follower grazing system described in Chapter 7 is particularly suitable in this situation, though it is rarely used in commercial practice.

Grazing ahead of the older cattle, the young calves have first pick of the grass but there is still sufficient grazing to support the performance of the finishing cattle. The cattle are grazed around five or six paddocks or small fields. The decision to move is made when sward height in the followers' paddock falls to 8 cm.

It is difficult to get good performance from the latest-born calves and, as well as allowing them to graze selectively, it may be necessary to feed 1.5 kg per day of supplementary concentrates at least until mid-season.

Turning out the target of 2500 kg total liveweight per hectare is not far short of five calves plus five finishing cattle per hectare. The cattle need about half the total grassland area until aftermaths from the first silage cut become available, then two thirds. At the time of the first silage cut growth on any paddocks not needed for grazing should be cut for silage.

After mid-season when, hopefully, marketing of finished cattle gets under way leader/follower grazing is disbanded. The calves should always be given priority for fresh, clean aftermath grazing. Even so their daily gain target can be set no higher then 0.7–0.8 kg. By comparison the finishing cattle should gain 1.0–1.1 kg per day.

The leader/follower system assists worm control but anthelmintic treatment is still necessary for the younger age group.

The silage requirement of grass beef is high because of the dependence on silage during the store winter. Needing half the total grassland area for grazing early in the season puts silage making under pressure. It is best to operate a three-cut regime and, by intensive grazing management, to release as much grassland as possible for cutting.

The calves are housed in the autumn and fed a store ration of silage with minimal supplementary concentrates. The aim is to exploit compensatory growth in the following grazing season which is done by restricting winter gains. The lower the winter gain, the higher the grazing gain. Time comes into the equation too and the best balance between winter and summer performance, consistent with starting to market finished cattle in July, is a daily gain through the winter of 0.6–0.7 kg, depending on breed type. Then at turnout in the spring cattle are well grown but lean and grow rapidly on high quality grazing.

Overfeeding concentrates during the store winter, which is a common mistake, wastes money because it merely depresses daily gains during the grazing season.

Achieving the grass finishing target of 1.0–1.1 kg per day is very important so that marketing can start in July and reduce cattle numbers in step with declining grass availability and quality. Failure to meet this timetable increases the risk of cattle failing to finish off grass. Worse still it increases competition with the calves whose performance is so sensitive to adverse conditions.

An early start to marketing is so important that early maturity is a big

Table 10.11 Targets for steers in grass beef from three months of age.

	Friesian/Holstein	Hereford × Friesian	Limousin/Belgian Blue × Friesian	Charolais/Simmental × Friesian
Reared calf (kg)	110	110	110	120
Daily gain (kg)				
– rearing winter	0.7	0.7	0.7	0.8
– first grazing season	0.7	0.7	0.7	0.8
– store winter	0.7	0.6	0.7	0.7
– grass finishing	1.0	1.0	1.0	1.1
– overall	0.78	0.75	0.78	0.85
Cereal (tonnes)	0.5	0.4	0.5	0.6
Silage (tonnes, 25% DM)	5.0	5.0	5.0	5.5
Stocking (cattle/ha)	2.5	3.0	2.5	2.3
Slaughter age (months)	22	20	23	22
Slaughter weight (kg)	550	500	575	610
Carcase weight	290	270	320	335
Main carcase class (EUROP)	O+4L	R4L	–U3*	–U4L

* Belgian Blue × Friesian U+3

advantage (see Chapter 7). So Hereford × Friesian steers and heifers of all breed types have an advantage over late maturing Friesian/Holstein and continental breed × Friesian steers. Of course heifers have daily gains and slaughter weights 10–12 per cent lower than steers, but their lower cost and the ability to stock them more heavily mean that gross margin per hectare can rival steers.

Table 10.11 presents performance targets for steers in grass beef. There are no results from commercial farms to validate the targets or identify financial pressure points. However, by analogy with other systems a high dependence on silage in the store winter, high daily gains in the first and second grazing seasons and high stocking rate are likely to be the key components of profitable production.

Marketing

At the high slaughter age of grass beef the gaunt conformation of the Friesian/Holstein is at its worst and price penalties can be very severe. However, there is a good demand for all types of beef breed × Friesians, including heifers. Recently the price of heifer beef has moved much closer to the steer price. Especially with heifers, the main concern should be to ensure that they are slaughtered before they get into overfat class 4H and suffer a price penalty.

There are grassland management pressures to market cattle as soon as possible. The seasonal price trend adds to this with prices falling 2–4p per kg liveweight between July and October.

11   Suckled Calf Production

In agriculture few scenes are more appealing than the beef cow suckling and tending her calf, and a fine beef bull going about his business. It conforms well with the modern vision of environmental conservation. And at the macho level the beef cow is the foundation of the cowboy tradition which lives on in rangeland countries.

The impression that beef herd management is a simple business is far from the truth. It confuses the low level of supervision of cows (easy care) with the high standards of organisation and management needed for profitable production. If anything suckler herds are more complicated to manage than beef finishing enterprises because reproduction, lactation and growth all contribute to the output of the enterprise.

Suckled calf production is not very efficient energetically. However, cows can be kept on land which is not suitable or not needed for milk production or arable cropping. In Britain the majority of cows are found in upland and hill areas which amount to 6.5 million hectares, more than a third of agricultural land which would be unused were it not for the herds of beef cows and flocks of sheep. Elsewhere beef herds are found in the rangelands of the Americas, Australia and in pastoral countries such as New Zealand.

In fact the suckler cow is more efficient as a producer of protein than appears at first sight. In marginal areas the calf is produced from land which would not otherwise contribute to human food supplies. And although the calf must be finished on better land the area required is small in relation to the total weight of lean beef produced. Moreover, there is a relatively small input of cereals, protein and fossil fuels.

Traditionally British suckler producers have sold weaned calves 6–12 months old at the autumn sales. However, the tendency is to intensify herd output, either by overwintering calves for sale as stores in the spring, or by feeding them through to slaughter. One of the latest developments is rapid finishing of suckled bull calves on a cereal beef diet. Nevertheless, on most upland farms the scarcity of winter feed dictates that calves are sold in the autumn.

On upland farms the integration of cattle and sheep improves not only grassland management but also profits. The relative importance of cattle tends to increase as the land gets better. On high mountain farms sheep outnumber cows by 20 to 1, if there are any cows at all. On fenced upland farms there may be only five or fewer ewes to each cow.

With the shortage of beef rearing stock in Britain consequent on falling dairy cow numbers in response to EEC milk quotas there is scope for suckler herd expansion. Indeed, cow numbers have increased since 1986 after a decade of decline and the suckler herd is currently growing at 4 per cent annually.

THE SUCKLER SYSTEM

The objective of the suckler herd is profitable production but the way it fits into the farm is important too. On hill and upland farms the role played by the herd in grassland management has benefits for the sheep flock. On arable farms the herd can utilise straw and arable by-products such as sugar beet tops and arable crop wastes, as well as playing an important part in the crop rotation.

The key planning decisions are the season of calving and whether calves are sold at the autumn sales, overwintered for sale as stores in the spring or fed through to slaughter. The intended disposal of calves interacts with calving season. Decisions depend on the available feeds, housing and labour.

Autumn-born calves are heavier at the autumn sales than those born in the spring and the higher output is reflected in a higher gross margin per cow. However, because spring-calving herds require lower inputs they can be stocked more heavily and the gross margin per hectare is similar to autumn calving.

Winter and summer calving also have their advocates. Calving in late winter can reduce winter feed costs and the calf is quite well grown in the spring and makes good use of grass. The problem is that cows calve indoors and that increases the risks of disease. With summer calving the calf is well grown in the autumn and winter feeding can be aimed at the calf saving cow feed costs. In practice the danger of summer calving is falling between two stools and incurring high feed costs but achieving only modest calf performance.

A comparison of performance and inputs for the different calving seasons is shown in Table 11.1.

The point has been made already that on tough upland and hill farms the scarcity of winter feeds dictates spring calving. Similarly on arable farms crop residues are, on average, of moderate quality and fit in best with spring

Table 11.1 Performance and inputs for different calving seasons in upland herds.

Calving season:	Spring	Summer	Autumn	Winter
Calf age at sale (months)	7	15	12	9
Calf daily gain (kg)	1.0	0.8	0.9	1.0
Calf weight at sale (kg)	265	425	375	325
Concentrates (kg) – cows	100	200	150	125
– calves	75	200	125	100
Silage (tonnes)	4.5	6.5	6.0	5.0
Stocking rate (cows/ha)	1.75	1.35	1.50	1.65

calving. If winter housing is limited again spring calving would be preferred, as it would be in slatted buildings which are not suitable for cows with calves at foot. If suckler bull beef production is contemplated it is easier to organise in the spring-calving herd.

On good land with plenty of high quality silage, adequate buildings and good stockmanship skills available through the winter, autumn calving is an attractive option. As well-grown yearlings the suckled calves can go straight into winter finishing.

Bigger farms may even decide to have complementary spring and autumn calving herds to utilise all resources to the full. The danger is that neither herd is managed well with late-calving cows shuttling between one herd and the other.

THE BULL

Choosing a bull for the suckler herd is a major decision both in terms of cost and influence. Good bulls are expensive but can more than repay their cost because half the genes in each calf come from the bull. Choice of breed and individual bull are equally important.

Bull breed

The discussion in Chapter 4 analysed the trade-offs which are involved in sire breed choice. The heavy, muscular continental breeds sire the fastest growing calves with the best conformation but they also cause the highest levels of dystocia.

British suckled calf producers have learned to manage the more difficult calvings caused by continental breeds such as the Charolais. As a result the Charolais is now the most important terminal sire breed used in commercial suckler herds, with substantial use of the Limousin and Simmental as well. However, easy calving breeds such as Angus or Hereford, and perhaps intermediate Limousins, would be preferred for heifer matings because of the higher level of dystocia at the first calving.

Effects of sire breed on preweaning performance carry through into the finishing period and have important effects on killing-out percentage, carcase quality and meat yield. These effects are reflected in prices paid at the suckled calf sales and at the bull sales.

Bull selection

There is as much variation among bulls within a breed as there is between breeds. So selection of the individual bull is extremely important. Performance and soundness are the key points.

The ideal bull works for several seasons siring progeny which are calved easily, grow rapidly and produce carcases of good shape with a high yield of saleable meat. It goes almost without saying that the bull must be fertile, active and have a reliable temperament.

It is difficult for a commercial buyer to get beneath the razzamatazz of a bull sale. The first job is to sort out the performance records because the presentation of these at sales leaves important questions unanswered. Do not be swayed by an exceptional but isolated absolute weight record. This may be more a tribute to the breeder's skill in rearing the bull than it is an expression of genetic potential. Remember, too, that overfed bulls, and there are too many of them at sales, must be slimmed down before they are fit to work.

If the bull has an MLC Beef Index Score set a standard of 120 points (100 is average) and look at the component records to confirm good all round performance. The calving difficulty score for the bull himself is a guide, albeit a crude one, to the likely ease of calving of his progeny. It is probably at least as reliable as avoiding bulls with heavy shoulders believing them to cause more difficult calvings.

If only weight-for-age records are available find out from the breeder where the bull ranked among his herdmates as opposed to the comparison with breed average. Remember that a bull with a 400-day weight 100 kg above *herd* average is likely to sire progeny about 25 kg above average at the same age.

Bulls which meet the performance standard then need to be checked for soundness. Ask the breeder to demonstrate that the teeth meet the dental pad squarely and that the jaw is not under- or over-shot. The bull should be able to walk well, with sound feet and legs which are neither over-straight nor sickle-hocked. The testicles are not a reliable guide to fertility but bulls with small, uneven or soft testicles are best avoided. If temperament is bad the bull should be rejected whatever his other merits.

And finally, not first, bulls should be preferred which have good conformation, smoothly and thickly muscled but not overfat. If the bull which is finally purchased is good-looking in the sense of breed type and gives pleasure every time he is seen on the farm, that is an added bonus. But it is not worth bidding a high price for showring good looks.

Bull management

The young bull arriving on the commercial farm is sexually inexperienced, probably overweight and unused to his new surroundings. If possible he should not be put to work immediately but be given time to settle down, shed his show condition and be introduced to a cow in oestrus to demonstrate the ability to mount and serve.

In the first season the young bull should be given no more than 20–25 cows. Careful observation is necessary in case cows return to service because the bull is infertile or inactive. If there are any doubts a semen test is worthwhile though this is not an infallible guide to fertility.

During the first mating season the young bull is still growing and, serving each cow three or four times, is working hard. It is a good idea to feed the bull extra concentrates and he can usually be enticed away from the cows to do this.

After the first season the bull should be able to manage 30–40 cows in a mating period of 6–12 weeks.

The average working life of a bull is probably only three seasons which is not sufficient to cover a high purchase price. Herd life is sometimes ended prematurely by accidents or infertility. More often bull management is at fault.

Probably the commonest problem is overgrown feet which predispose the bull to injury. Annual or more frequent foot trimming is essential and if a crush with a foot trimming attachment is not available it is well worth calling in a specialist contractor to do the job.

The other common problem is that bulls become bad-tempered and dangerous to handle. This may be unavoidable but it helps if the bull pen is at the centre of farmyard matters and that time is spent on regular handling so that the bull does not spend his days in dismal isolation. At the same time it is important to be aware of the potential dangers so bulls must be handled with respect and housed in pens constructed to conform with safety standards.

In summer bull(s) should be grazed in a well-fenced paddock. If the bulls have been separated during the winter they should be brought together in tight confinement so that a pecking order can be sorted out without serious fighting.

Suckler herd owners are requested not to run bulls with suckler cows in fields crossed by public footpaths but if they do warning signs should be posted and, if possible, the footpath temporarily diverted.

AI

Buying and maintaining a bull is expensive and for the smaller herd AI is usually a cheaper alternative. If the AI bulls are of exceptional quality and have been screened by progeny testing they may be used in bigger herds on merit. And for heifer matings AI offers the possibility of using a continental breed bull proven to be easy calving.

Despite its theoretical advantages AI is not much used in suckled calf production. Farms are not organised for AI, particularly when the herd is grazing outlying fields, and oestrus detection is less successful than in dairy herds because beef cows are inspected less frequently and seem to be less demonstrable in oestrus than dairy cows. Nevertheless there are large herds which use AI successfully.

Good oestrus detection is the key to good AI management. The cow is in full heat when she will stand to be mounted. For visual oestrus detection cows need to be checked at least three times a day, and even if tail paint is used or heat mount detectors are stuck on the rump, twice-daily inspection is necessary.

Some of the producers who have used AI most successfully have abandoned visual inspection and use a vasectomised teaser bull fitted with a marker attached to a harness to detect oestrus. There is still the cost of running a bull with the herd but a young bull can be slaughtered for bull beef after the mating period, minimising the cost.

The use of a vasectomised bull is probably cheaper and more effective than AI based on oestrus synchronisation.

Various synchronisation procedures have been developed. One uses prostaglandin, a hormone-like substance which causes regression of the corpus luteum and prompts oestrus. The treatment procedure is:

Day 1 (Monday or Thursday):   Inject prostaglandin.
Day 12 (Friday or Monday):   Inject prostaglandin.
Day 15 (Monday or Thursday):   First insemination.
Day 16 (Tuesday or Friday):   Second insemination.

An alternative approach is to insert a progesterone-releasing intravaginal device (PRID) which is removed on day 12 and synchronises oestrus for double insemination on days 15 and 16. Double insemination results in a sufficient increase in the conception rate to be economic.

Oestrus synchronisation does not really have a place in cow matings because, even in a herd with a short calving period, a rather small proportion of the herd is suitable for treatment. However, some producers do use synchronisation for block-calving heifers. It is important to recognise that the natural variation in gestation length and returns to service mean that calvings are not well synchronised. So even for heifer matings by AI, consideration should be given to using a vasectomised bull and single insemination rather than a synchronisation procedure.

In herds large enough to justify the purchase of a bull for natural service the arguments for using AI are not compelling. Provided uncompromising performance standards are set for natural service bulls, progeny performance will rival closely the best AI bulls. And herd management is much simpler.

THE COW

The cow is the workhorse of suckled calf production, expected to cope with seasonal variations in feed supply and to produce and rear a calf every year. Indeed, the weight of calf produced per cow per year is closely related to herd profitability.

Cow type

It comes as a surprise to many cattlemen in Britain that in rangeland countries such as the USA the superior performance of crossbred cows over purebreds is still being tested experimentally and crossbreeding systems developed to exploit hybrid vigour. The British suckler herd is dominated by crossbred cows and the benefits of hybrid vigour are accepted as a matter of course. It is also a surprise that the French suckler herd is mostly purebred taking no advantage of hybrid vigour.

Compared to purebreds first cross (F1) calves survive better and grow into females with earlier puberty, higher conception rates and easier calving.

The cumulative advantage in calf weaning weight to the crossbred cow over the pure parent breeds is 25 per cent per cow mated which is an enormous margin of superiority. It is probably added to by greater longevity.

The traditional source of crossbred cows in Britain was, and still is to some extent, the mountain breeds. The Blue Grey (a blue roan bred by crossing a White Shorthorn bull with a Galloway cow) has a legendary reputation and other crosses such as Beef Shorthorn × Highland have their devotees. Another type of Blue Grey was produced in Ireland by crossing Angus bulls with Dairy Shorthorns but the supply has largely dried up as Dairy Shorthorns have been replaced by the Friesian/Holstein.

In the mid 1960s these traditional crossbreds started to be augmented by Hereford × Friesians and to a lesser extent Angus × Friesians. For the last decade the Hereford × Friesian has been the staple suckler cow in Britain.

When the Hereford × Friesian cow first came to prominence it was assumed that its lowland origins and performance characteristics would limit use to lowland and better upland farms. On the contrary it is remarkable over just how wide a range of environments the Hereford × Friesian has been successful.

Overall the performance of Hereford × Friesian cows is similar to the admirable Blue Grey (Table 11.2). The Hereford × Friesian is slightly heavier than the Blue Grey and has slightly poorer reproductive efficiency, but calf weaning weight is higher and the annual production of calf weaning weight produced per unit cow weight is similar for the two cow types. Angus × Friesians are also used successfully as suckler cows with similar weight and performance to the Blue Grey.

The popularity of Hereford and Angus × Friesians has been undermined in recent years by the increasing influence of the Holstein on cow conformation. Suckled calf producers, always very conscious of good conformation, have seen a deterioration in the conformation of their cows and believe it has now reached the point where it shows through in the calf.

Almost certainly the situation has been overstated but there is no smoke without fire. So, while many suckler herd owners continue to use Angus and Hereford × Friesian cows, others are trying better conformation continental breed × Friesian cows, especially Limousin × Friesian and Simmental × Friesian.

Such field records as there are (Table 11.3) indicate that the continental breed × Friesian cows produce calves with heavier weaning weights which make a higher price per kg than calves out of British breed × Friesians because of better conformation. But the results should be treated with caution because it looks as though the continental breed × Friesian cows were in the hands of top producers.

Table 11.2 Comparative performance of Hereford × Friesian (H × F) and Blue Grey (BG) cows. (Source: MLC)

Sire breed:	Charolais		Hereford		Angus	
Cow type:	H × F	BG	H × F	BG	H × F	BG
Live calves per 100 cows	94.9	95.6	98.2	98.7	98.5	98.9
Calving interval (days)	378	369	372	367	370	366
Calf weight at 250 days (kg)	294	278	249	234	236	220
Annual calf output (kg/cow)	269	265	240	223	231	217
Annual calf output per 50 kg cow weight* (kg)	26.9	29.3	23.9	25.0	23.1	24.0

* Cow weight: Hereford × Friesian 500 kg; Blue Grey 450 kg.

Higher weaning weights and better conformation would be expected from calves out of continental breed-cross cows but at what, if any, cost to cow efficiency because of higher cow weight? Research in the USA shows that the higher output of heavier cows just balances their higher feed requirements so that differences in overall efficiency are small and not important when the predominant feed is low grade forage. Then choice of cow size depends on being able to provide the feed needed to support higher productivity.

Choice of sire breed interacts with cow type. Heavy sire breeds mated to medium-weight cows are much more efficient than the reverse.

When commercial embryo transfer becomes available a new situation arises because the cow need not contribute any genes to the calf. Therefore the cow could be bred solely for maternal qualities – ease of calving, regularity of breeding, milk yield and longevity. The logical approach would be to breed the smallest cow capable of delivering the genetic potential of the calf. This might be done by breeding a crossbred cow harnessing the ultra easy calving and good milk production of the Jersey, allied to the adaptability to seasonal fluctuations in nutrition of the Angus, which has the added advantage of being polled. Or the outstanding maternal qualities and longevity of the French Salers breed might be built into a crossbred cow.

COMPACT CALVING

A compact calving period is extremely important to profitable suckled calf production. The aim should be to complete calvings in a period no longer than 10 weeks, preferably less.

With a compact calving period rationing on a herd basis meets the needs of individual cows without some being underfed and others overfed because they are at different stages of production. In a short calving period the supervision of calvings can be better organised with less frayed nerves and fewer calf losses. And at weaning calves are even in weight and are easier to batch into sale or feeding groups. There are none of the late-born calves which sell so badly.

It is important to recognise that a compact calving period is a sign of high conception rate. This is fundamental to good reproductive efficiency and Table 11.4 shows the general relationship between conception and duration of the calving period.

In a long drawn-out calving period late calving cows are at a serious disadvantage. They are expected to conceive at their first oestrus early in lactation when conception rates are at their lowest. The net result is that

Table 11.3 Field comparison of continental breed cross suckler cows with British breed crosses.
(Source: *MLC Beef Yearbook*, 1988.)

	Continental crosses	British crosses
Cow performance (per 100 cows mated)		
Live calves born	90	90
Calf mortality	2	4
Calves purchased	1	3
Calves reared	89	89
Barren cows	5	8
Calf performance		
Age at sale (days)	272	260
Daily gain (kg)	1.04	0.96
Weight at sale (kg)	325	288
Sale price (p/kg)	118	111
Feeds and stocking rate		
Cow concentrates (kg)	138	158
Calf concentrates (kg)	97	73
Silage (tonnes)	4.1	3.8
Other feeds (tonnes)	1.0	1.2
Stocking (cows per ha)	1.78	1.94

poor conception rates worsen progressively so that late calvers get later and later.

In a herd with an extended calving period the first action must be to cull late calvers and replace them with heifers calving early in the period. Indeed in most suckler herds the first priority in culling policy should be getting rid of late calvers.

In a herd calving over several months culling all the late calvers to reduce the calving period to, say, six weeks might mean selling up to a third of the herd which is drastic action. However, if late calvers are sold with calves at foot or culls are sold for cow beef in early summer when prices are high, the

Table 11.4 Relationship between conception rate and duration of the calving period.

Conception rate (%)	Calving period (months)
60	<3
50	3–4
40	4–5
35	5–6

income goes a long way to funding the cost of replacement heifers. Moreover, replacement costs are offset further by the value of increased weaning weight which occurs because the average calving date is brought forward.

Some producers may decide it is prudent to shorten the calving period gradually, spreading the extra culling over two seasons. Other herds tackle the problem by having both autumn and spring calving herds with late calvers transferred from one to the other. This is fine if the two herds can be justified on profit considerations but the practice does tend to obscure the cost of poor late-calving performance.

Once a compact calving period has been achieved through culling it is essential to take action to ensure that it stays compact. The bulling period should be restricted to six weeks and the bulls removed on schedule, not left for 'a bit longer'. As mentioned earlier it is essential to watch out for bulls which are lazy or infertile. Heifers should be mated to calve early because there is always the risk of delayed rebreeding after the first calving. Routine manual or ultrasonic pregnancy diagnosis should be used to identify barren cows as soon as possible. And finally, good supervision of calvings can reduce the number of difficult calvings which cause delayed rebreeding.

In addition to these organisational matters it is vital that cow nutrition is managed so that body condition is good at mating and that conception rates are high. Only then can a compact calving period be sustained without recourse to continued high culling rates.

NUTRITION AND BODY CONDITION

Nutrition has important effects on reproductive efficiency, especially during the period leading up to mating. If the cow is too thin at mating, on a low nutrient intake or both, she may fail to get in calf altogether or, at best, conception is delayed.

Body condition is a very sensitive barometer of nutritional status. If cows are fed too little to produce the milk demanded by the calf they draw on body reserves and become thinner. On the other hand, if feed is in excess of the needs of milk production cows become fatter.

Beef specialists at the East of Scotland College of Agriculture have developed a systematic method of scoring body condition so that changes can be charted and manipulated throughout the year.

The method of scoring is to grip the loin with the fingers on top and the thumb curled under the ledge formed by the transverse processes of the backbone (Figure 11.1). The inside of the thumb is used to feel the fat

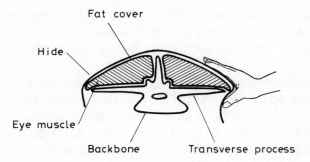

Fig. 11.1 The technique of body condition scoring.

thickness over the ends of the transverse processes.

Body condition is scored 1 (very thin) to 5 (very fat) as follows:

Score 1: Spine prominent and the transverse processes feel sharp to the touch with no detectable fat cover.

Score 2: The bony transverse processes can still be felt but they are rounded due to a thin covering of fat.

Score 3: Transverse processes can only be felt with firm pressure.

Score 4: Transverse processes cannot be felt even with firm pressure.

Score 5: The cow is obviously over-fat.

In cases of doubt, additional guidance can be gained by feeling the fat layer over the ribs with the flat of the hand and pressing with the fingers either side of the tailhead to feel the fat cover there.

Condition scoring can be quickly learned and, though periodic handling of cattle is necessary, once the scale of scores is familiar a good idea of cow condition can be gained by close visual observation.

The general relationship between body condition score and reproductive efficiency, expressed as calving interval, is shown in Figure 11.2.

Table 11.5 Target condition score for suckler cows.

Season	Target score	Stage of production	
	1 (thin) to 5 (fat)	Spring calver	Autumn calver
Spring	2	Calving	Pregnant/suckling
Summer	2½	Mating	Weaning
Autumn	3	Weaning	Calving
Winter	2½	Pregnant/dry	Mating

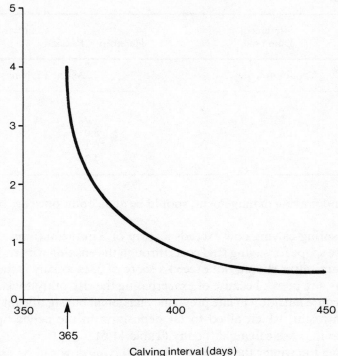

Fig. 11.2 General relationship between body condition score and calving interval. (Source: MLC.)

The implications of condition score go far beyond the description of nutritional status at mating. A series of target scores can be proposed (Table 11.5) which are used to manage feeding levels throughout the year.

The critical target is the condition score at mating. The cow must come into oestrus and conceive within three months of calving or production is disrupted with damaging effects on profitability.

Whether cows calve in the spring or autumn the target condition score at turnout in the spring is 2. At this time the spring calver is milking hard in early lactation but on good quality spring grass will probably gain condition to a score of 2½ by mid-summer. Even at a condition score of 2 on high quality grazing nutrient intake is high enough to allow normal conception. This contrasts with the autumn calver which mates in mid-winter and must attain the condition score of 2½ or conception is put at risk.

Both spring and autumn calvers gain condition through the summer and,

Table 11.6 Relationship between body condition and calving difficulty.
(Source: MLC)

Sire breed: Dam type:	Charolais Hereford × Friesian	Blue Grey
Condition score	Assisted calvings (%)	
2	6.7	4.0
2½	7.7	5.9
3	8.0	6.3
3½	10.1	7.0
4	14.3	10.1

with sound grazing management, should be at a condition score of 3 by the autumn.

If the spring-calving cow exceeds a score of 3 in the autumn that offers even more scope for saving feed costs through the ensuing winter. However, the autumn calver should not exceed a score of 3, especially if she is in calf to a heavy sire breed, because of exacerbating the risk of dystocia. This can occur because nutrition in late pregnancy has small but significant effects on calf birthweight, which allied to fat deposition in the pelvic opening, is enough to increase calving difficulty (Table 11.6).

Through the winter the pregnant spring-calving cow can be underfed to lose a unit of condition score as a means of cheapening winter feeding. Higher levels of feeding are needed for the autumn calver to support lactation and to be sure that condition score is 2½ through the bulling period. Once autumn calvers are safely in calf they can be allowed to lose a further ½ unit of condition by turnout.

Although mating is the crucial point in the production cycle it is probably true that meeting the target score of 2 at turnout is the key to keeping on target throughout the year whilst minimising cow feed costs. If autumn calvers are too thin at turnout decisive action is necessary to give them a chance to recover during the summer, for example by bringing forward the weaning date.

Milk production

Autumn calvers, in particular, are expected to support milk yield partly by utilising body reserves – 'milking off their backs'. Cows calving at the target condition score of 3 are better able to do this than thinner cows calving at a score of 2. Nevertheless current energy intake is always important to milk yield as evidenced by the jump of about 4 kg per day in milk when cows are turned out to spring grazing.

Cow feeding

Dr Ian Wright and Dr Angus Russell working at the Macaulay Land Use Research Institute in Scotland have used the management of condition score as the basis of cow feeding. They have calculated that a loss of one unit of condition score releases the equivalent of 3200 MJ dietary ME and that 6500 MJ ME need to be fed for a gain of one unit score. This information is extremely useful in designing winter rations for suckler cows.

For example, the pregnant spring calving Hereford × Friesian or Blue Grey has an ME requirement of 9600 MJ over a five-month feeding period. Allowed to lose $\frac{1}{2}$ unit of condition score (the other $\frac{1}{2}$ unit being lost in the period calving to turnout) body reserves supply 1600 MJ leaving the diet to supply 8000 MJ ME or 53 MJ ME per day. This is a modest daily requirement easily supplied by silage alone or rations based on plain or ammonia-treated straw supplemented with concentrates.

The autumn calving cow needs a higher level of feeding. For the three

Table 11.7 Specimen winter rations for suckler cows (500 kg liveweight).

Silage: 25% DM, 10MJ ME per kg DM.
Barley: 86% DM, 12.8 MJ ME per kg DM.
Barley straw: 86% DM, 6.5 MJ ME per kg DM.
Concentrates: 86% DM, 12 MJ ME per kg DM.

Period	Components	Daily ration (kg)
Autumn calving cow		
Calving to mating	Silage	25
	Barley	2
Mating to turnout	Silage	25
	Barley	1
Spring calving cow		
Yarding to calving	Silage	25
	Barley straw	6
	Concentrates	2
Calving to turnout	Silage	25
	Barley	2

months from calving until mating the requirement for maintenance and 9 kg milk daily totals 9150 MJ ME of which 1600 MJ is supplied from body reserves. This leaves a total dietary requirement of 7550 MJ ME or 84 MJ ME per day which would be met by good quality silage supplemented by about 2 kg concentrates daily.

A selection of specimen winter rations is shown in Table 11.7. Vitamin and mineral supplementation is important. Magnesium supplementation is very important both for cows suckling calves on winter feeds and on grazed grass if, as is all too often the case, hypomagnesaemic tetany is a farm problem.

THE CALF

In the suckler herd the calf is the product and every effort must be made to ensure that it performs to its potential. Choice of herd sire and cow management are very important but so is the management of the calf itself.

Calving

Disease problems are minimised if cows can be calved outdoors. If not buildings should be cleaned out thoroughly as soon as they are vacated in the spring and calving boxes should be power-washed or steam-cleaned.

As soon as possible after calving, while it can still be caught easily, the calf should be fitted with an easily read plastic ear tag and the details recorded in a herd diary.

Milk

Colostrum is just as important to the suckled calf as it is to the dairy-bred calf and calves should be observed to see that they suckle regularly during the first day. Just in case a cow dies or lactation is delayed it is worth keeping a supply of deep-frozen colostrum.

The suckling power of the calf has a major influence on the milk yield of the cow. In general calves which are heavier at birth take more milk and grow faster. On average for each 1 kg increase in birthweight, weaning weight increases 6 kg.

The appetite for milk builds quickly during the first month and dominates performance even though calves show an interest in solid feeds from an early

Table 11.8 Milk yield and its contribution to suckled calf gains.
(Source: Constructed from experimental findings at the East of Scotland College of Agriculture and the Institute for Grassland and Animal Production, Hurley.)

Month	Hereford × Friesian		Blue Grey	
	Daily milk (kg)	% of calf gain from milk	Daily milk (kg)	% of calf gain from milk
Autumn calving cow				
1	7.8	100	7.0	100
2	8.8	95	8.0	85
3	9.0	68	8.2	60
4	8.5	54	7.0	45
5	7.5	43	6.0	35
6	6.5	35	5.0	30
7	7.0	32	5.5	23
8	5.0	25	4.0	15
9	4.5	15	2.5	8
Total yield	1970		1620	
Spring calving cow				
1	8.6	100	7.5	100
2	10.5	100	9.0	95
3	11.0	75	9.2	70
4	9.8	61	8.0	50
5	8.8	51	7.0	41
6	7.5	45	5.8	36
7	6.0	35	4.5	25
Total yield	1900		1555	

age. It is not until the third or fourth month that solid feed accounts for half the daily gain (Table 11.8).

Milk accounts for two-thirds of the preweaning gain of the spring-born calf. The calf's requirements and milk production by the cow are well-matched. Yield increases as spring grazing becomes available at a time when the calf needs more milk. Then from mid-season, as grazing deteriorates, milk yield declines in step with the declining requirements of the calf as it grazes more itself.

The autumn-born calf has a longer total suckling period but milk yield in the winter is not as high on conserved feeds as the grazing yield of the spring calving cow. However, there is a kick in milk yield when the autumn calver is turned out to grazing in the spring. By mid-summer the dependence of the calf on milk is low and many herds could with advantage wean sooner, giving the weaned calves the best aftermath grazing.

Creep feeding

It is preferable to creep feed calves concentrates direct rather than feed the cow with the inefficient two-stage process – concentrates into milk, milk into meat.

The spring-born calf may not need concentrates at all but from mid-season there is a case for creep feeding especially in a drought. The total amount fed is small at about 40 kg.

Creep feeding of autumn-born calves is essential. Again it is more efficient to feed concentrates to the calf than to the cow. But there is more to it than that. From the start a creep should be erected within the cattle building and calves enticed into it with palatable concentrate. The creep feed makes a significant contribution to daily gain. Later silage can be introduced so that calves can develop their forage intake without having to compete with the cows at the main feed trough.

The concentrate can be a simple home mix of 60 per cent cereal, 30 per cent flaked maize and 10 per cent soyabean meal plus vitamins and minerals or 15 per cent of a proprietary protein supplement mixed with 85 per cent cereal. Concentrate is fed *ad libitum* at first and then rationed at 2–2½ kg per day.

Creep feeding is discontinued at turnout but is resumed from late summer, especially if the calves are weaned at that time. The total concentrate input, winter and summer, is likely to be 150–200 kg.

Both with spring- and autumn-born calves, creep feeding in late summer sustains daily gain and improves the appearance of calves which brings better sale results. Also, where calves go on into winter finishing there is a smooth transition to the winter diet.

Castration

Before castrating male calves it is worth investigating the local market for entire males. Some auctions now have special sales for bull calves and they may command a premium over steers. Moreover, even during the pre-weaning period bulls grow 10 per cent faster than steers and so have higher sale weights.

In spring calving herds there is no need to separate bull and heifer calves. However, for herds calving in the autumn it is necessary to split cows with bull calves from those with heifers at about six months of age. In autumn-calving herds bull beef is really only practicable if the calving period is compact, otherwise the older bull calves annoy cows in oestrus late in the mating period and there is a risk of older heifer calves becoming pregnant.

If bull calves are castrated this should be carried out by three or four months of age using a scalpel or Burdizzo pliers. Beyond two months of age the British welfare regulations require castration to be carried out by a veterinary surgeon using an anaesthetic. If rubber rings are used they should be applied in the first week.

Weaning

Having nurtured the bond between cow and calf, it has to be broken at weaning and this needs to be done with the minimum of stress.

Weaning is easiest for the spring-born calf because it can be timed to coincide with sale or yarding. However, autumn-born calves need to be weaned by the tenth month which still leaves a further period of grazing. Probably the best approach is to put the cows and weaned calves in adjacent paddocks within sight and sound of each other. Ideally the calves are put on fresh aftermaths which they can graze selectively and when they are moved on the cows follow behind to clear up.

Drying off cows does not usually present problems, though it is wise to restrict grazing for the first week or so. If mastitis is a herd problem dry cow therapy with a long-acting antibiotic may be necessary.

Diseases

Scouring and pneumonia are the most common calfhood diseases.

It is important to learn to differentiate between the loose dung of a calf which is suckling more milk than is really good for it and infectious scouring. Early treatment is nececessary or losses can be severe. Scouring is at its worst when cows and calves are housed and on problem farms it may be necessary to vaccinate the cows to confer immunity on the calves.

Pneumonia is also largely a problem of housed cattle though it can also occur outdoors on damp autumn days. Early recognition of symptoms and prompt treatment are essential if losses and permanent impairment of performance are to be avoided.

It is surprising how widespread copper deficiency is in calves. A copper problem should be suspected whenever ill-thrift occurs. On many farms routine copper injections have to be given.

GRASSLAND MANAGEMENT

Grassland management contributes to cattle performance through the quality of grazing and conserved forage and to gross margin per hectare through the stocking rate adopted.

MLC Beefplan results from commercial suckler herds show a characteristic range in stocking rates (Table 11.9). Clearly many producers could increase stocking rates without adjustment of N fertiliser inputs. The average rate of N fertiliser use was quite low and on many farms there is scope for using more N fertiliser to increase stocking rate. On some farms a switch to clover swards is a possibility.

Good grazing management is essential if high daily gains are to be achieved in calves and cows are to gain the 0.5 kg per day necessary to increase condition score from 2 at turnout to 3 by the autumn.

Cows gain most weight early in the season at a sward height of 8–10 cm but at this height selective grazing leaves the sward patchy with seed head development. So the recommendation is that sward height for cows and calves should be controlled at 8 cm in the early part of the grazing season but be allowed to increase to 10 cm later on when the risk of seed head development is past.

Cows and calves are set stocked on the grazing area, ideally with about 25 per cent fenced off as a buffer area. As much of the grazing buffer as possible

Table 11.9 MLC Beefplan results from commercial suckler herds, 1987. (Source: *MLC Beef Yearbook*, 1988.)

	Bottom third	Average gross margin per hectare	Top third
Lowland herds – autumn calving			
Stocking (cows/ha)	1.3	1.7	2.0
N fertiliser (kg N/ha)	139	141	158
Lowland herds – spring calving			
Stocking (cows/ha)	2.0	2.1	2.5
N fertiliser (kg N/ha)	120	134	145
Upland herds – autumn calving			
Stocking (cows/ha)	1.0	1.3	1.5
N fertiliser (kg N/ha)	90	119	123
Upland herds – spring calving			
Stocking (cows/ha)	1.4	1.6	1.9
N fertiliser (kg N/ha)	122	115	145

is cut for silage at the time of the first cut. But if necessary part or all of it is grazed in a late or dry season to assist in sward height control.

At a fertiliser application of 200 kg N per hectare the target stocking rate at turnout should be 2.5 tonnes cow + calf weight (3+ for autumn calvers or 4 for spring calvers) gradually falling to 1.5 tonnes per hectare in the late season as aftermaths are added to the grazing area.

The spring calving herd with a requirement of about 5 tonnes silage per cow needs half the grassland area for first cut silage, if possible with a second cut from part of the area. Surprisingly, although the autumn calving herd needs 6 tonnes of silage per cow (because of consumption by the calf) the stocking rate is lower and cutting half the area still supplies the bulk of the silage requirements.

The control of parasitic worms is much less of a problem in suckled calf production than when young dairy bred cattle are stocked heavily. It is worth dosing cows with an anthelmintic at yarding to limit the eggs they deposit on pasture the next spring. Autumn-born calves should be dosed at weaning and moved to clean aftermath grazing. Spring-born calves should also be dosed at weaning if they are to be retained on the farm.

TARGETS AND PERFORMANCE

Targets of performance for lowland and upland suckler herds are presented in Table 11.10. In hill herds it would be realistic to expect 5 per cent fewer calves weaned and 10 per cent lower calf gains.

MLC Beefplan results from commercial lowland and upland suckler herds (Tables 11.11 and 11.12) show that high gross margin per cow was a product of high calf output – a high percentage of calves reared and high daily gain – achieved at below average concentrate input because of a higher dependence on forage feeds. To add to this top third stocking rates were 15–20 per cent above average so that gross margin per hectare was 40–45 per cent higher than average. Bottom third performance was bad all round with inevitable effects on financial results.

An important message to emerge from the MLC records is that in spring-calving herds it pays to retain calves for sale as stores in the spring rather than take them to the autumn sales (Table 11.13). Part of the reason for this is the higher sale price per kg in the spring. It looks as though this would be financially advantageous even if it meant reducing cow numbers to release winter feed and space in the buildings. In the same vein it is worth budgeting the consequences of carrying calves through to slaughter.

Table 11.10 Targets for suckled calf production in lowland and upland herds.

Calving season:	Continental sire breeds, e.g.: Charolais, Limousin, Simmental		British sire breeds, e.g.: Angus, Hereford	
	Autumn	Spring	Autumn	Spring
Calving period (weeks)	12	8	12	8
Calves reared per 100 cows bulled	92	92	95	95
Silage (tonnes)	6	5	6	5
Cow concentrates (kg)	250	100	250	100
Calf concentrate (kg)	150	50	100	50
Stocking (cows/ha)				
– lowland	2.0	2.5	2.0	2.5
– upland	1.5	2.0	1.5	2.0
Calf daily gain (kg)	1.0	1.1	0.9	1.0
Rearing period (months)	10	7	10	7
Calf sale weight (kg)	350	280	315	260

Table 11.11 MLC Beefplan results from commercial lowland suckler herds, 1987. (Source: *MLC Beef Yearbook*, 1988.)

	Autumn calving herds			Spring calving herds		
	Bottom third	Average gross margin per hectare	Top third	Bottom third	Average gross margin per hectare	Top third
Gross margin per cow (£)	162	230	280	151	187	220
Gross margin per ha (£)	207	382	557	294	391	557
Herd replacements (per 100 cows)	14	16	19	18	20	22
Calving period* (weeks)	15	12	12	18	12	12
Per 100 cows bulled						
– live calves born	89	90	93	91	91	92
– calf mortality	8	5	5	7	6	4
– calves purchased	6	4	4	5	5	4
– calves reared	87	89	92	89	92	92
Silage (tonnes)	4.9	4.7	4.9	2.8	2.7	2.8
Other feeds (tonnes)	0.6	0.9	1.0	0.9	1.0	1.1
Cow concentrates (kg)	226	189	134	110	114	95
Calf concentrates (kg)	147	235	154	111	94	90
Stocking (cows/ha)	1.3	1.7	2.0	2.0	2.1	2.5
Calf daily gain (kg)	0.85	0.88	0.90	0.87	0.93	1.00
Rearing period (days)	350	372	375	247	244	239
Calf sale weight (kg)	330	369	375	255	266	279

* 90 per cent of calvings

Table 11.12 MLC Beefplan results from commercial upland suckler herds, 1987. (Source: *MLC Beef Yearbook*, 1988.)

	Autumn calving herds			Spring calving herds		
	Bottom third	Average gross margin per hectare	Top third	Bottom third	Average gross margin per hectare	Top third
Gross margin per cow (£)	214	271	336	155	223	269
Gross margin per ha (£)	210	350	501	209	352	498
Herd replacements (per 100 cows)	19	19	21	19	19	15
Calving period* (weeks)	17	14	12	13	12	12
Per 100 cows bulled						
– live calves born	90	91	92	88	90	93
– calf mortality	6	4	2	6	4	3
– calves purchased	6	7	4	6	4	4
– calves reared	90	94	94	88	91	94
Silage (tonnes)	5.9	6.4	6.6	4.2	4.0	4.4
Other feeds (tonnes)	0.5	0.5	0.5	0.6	0.6	0.4
Cow concentrates (kg)	192	159	136	138	122	104
Calf concentrates (kg)	190	245	129	126	65	77
Stocking (cows/ha)	1.0	1.3	1.5	1.4	1.6	1.9
Calf daily gain (kg)	0.86	0.90	0.95	0.81	0.87	0.91
Rearing period (days)	335	348	352	235	247	269
Calf sale weight (kg)	327	354	373	230	255	285

* 90 per cent of calvings

Table 11.13 MLC Beefplan results for spring calving herds selling calves in the autumn or spring.
(Source: *MLC Beef Yearbook*, 1988.)

	Lowland herds		Upland herds	
	Autumn sale	Spring sale	Autumn sale	Spring sale
Gross margin per cow (£)	164	245	202	285
Gross margin per ha (£)	377	451	358	412
Age at sale (days)	213	375	207	344
Sale weight (kg)	245	359	245	312
Sale price (p/kg)	113	120	118	120
Cow concentrates (kg)	135	99	132	108
Calf concentrates (kg)	24	300	44	262
Stocking (cows/ha)	2.3	1.8	1.8	1.5

DOUBLE SUCKLING

The suckler cow is perfectly capable of producing sufficient milk to rear two calves. Double suckling would bring a considerable increase in output and allow the intensification of suckled calf production. However, on the farm the potential benefits seem difficult to realise.

Double suckling can only be economic in herds calving in the summer or autumn. In the spring-calving herd the suckling period is relatively short and the set-on calf is so expensive that there is insufficient value added to increase the gross margin significantly. Even with the longer suckling period in autumn-calving herds the cost of the set-on calf is critical. In the summer of 1989, for example, a Charolais × Friesian calf weighing 55 kg would have cost about £225 and at equivalent store prices the calf would not regain its original purchase price until it weighed 150 kg.

Inevitably with two calves suckling instead of one, the average growth rate of the calves is less than for single suckling, even if a milky Hereford × Friesian cow is used. This may mean two moderate calves in place of one good one. Further, if the set-on calf introduces diseases such as E. coli scour or salmonellosis these can spread like wildfire.

Whenever purchased calves are introduced for suckling the temperament of the cows is important. There is no point in persevering with nervous or bad-tempered cows because the system cannot bear the labour cost or frayed nerves. Unfortunately temperament can only be tested by experience and failures are expensive.

The extra drain on the cow of double suckling requires increased feed intake during the first three months so that the body condition of the cow does not slip below the critical mating target. This applies even more strongly to cows which are used to multiple suckle up to four calves.

REPLACEMENT HEIFERS

Replacement rates in suckler herds are typically 15–18 per cent. Apart from replacing the occasional cow which dies the main replacement is of cows which are culled.

Barrenness and late calving are the two main causes of culling. Also, once cows reach 10 years of age they should be culled before calf performance falls off and the cows become thin and lose their cull value. Good cull cows command high prices for meat if sold in good condition at the peak of the market in spring and early summer. The sale proceeds go a long way to financing the replacement heifer.

The most immediate but most expensive method of replacement is to wait until it is known how many heifers are needed and then either buy them on the point of calving (down-calvers) or with calves at foot. The cost is high but calves are produced straight away when they are wanted. It is wise not to buy older cows because of their uncertain disease status.

Much more sensible as a replacement policy is the purchase of well grown yearling or bulling heifers which are then mated to calve early in the calving period. At this age heifers can be selected which are functionally sound and not prone to overfatness. A 10 per cent surplus needs to be purchased to allow for any which do not get in calf. Surplus heifers are sold for slaughter.

There is a temptation to retain heifers from the previous crop of suckled calves. Whilst this may be acceptable in some circumstances, there are drawbacks which need to be recognised. In particular, if the heifers are sired by a heavy continental breed they will grow into heavy mature cows and have less milk than F1 beef breed × Friesians. This is a recipe for high feed costs but modest performance. In addition, the heifers cannot be mated back to their sire if he is still in use for fear of inbreeding depression. And pursuing this course can lead eventually to replacements with too high a proportion of blood from the terminal sire breed and a loss of hybrid vigour.

In proposing these arguments clear distinction must be made between retaining slaughter generation heifers from the suckler herd and breeding F1 crossbred females such as the Blue Grey specifically for use as suckler cows.

The least expensive method of suckler herd replacement is to rear beef breed × Friesian calves purchased as two-week-old calves or reared calves at three months. This approach requires forward planning because replacement numbers need to be estimated two to three years ahead. It is only possible if feed supplies and buildings are available on the farm for the two or three generations of heifers being reared at any time.

The usual practice is to purchase 20–25 per cent more calves than are needed to give scope for selection, to take account of breeding failures and to allow for errors in estimating requirements.

On lowland and upland farms in Britain, in pastoral countries and on better quality rangelands, calving heifers for the first time at two years of age is both feasible and desirable. Compared to first calving at three years, heifers calved at two years produce a modest first calf but an extra calf over their lifetime.

Not all breed types are equally suitable for calving at two years old. For example, in the major breed comparison at Clay Center in the USA, the British breeds reached puberty at about a year of age, a full month earlier than continental breed crosses such as the Charolais. The consequence of this was a considerably higher proportion of British breed heifers in calf at 18 months of age. The continental breed crosses are happier calving first at 30 months. Indeed, French producers working with purebred late maturing breeds generally calve them first at three years old.

One argument for delaying first calving is that the heifer is better grown and reaches mature weight sooner. The reverse argument is more relevant, that two year calving restricts growth and delays the attainment of mature size, thereby reducing feed costs. But, remember that after the first calving feeding must be good enough for the heifer to reach the target condition score of $2\frac{1}{2}$ at mating or rebreeding may be delayed. In any event rebreeding tends to be delayed in heifers which is why they need to be calved early in the calving period.

If beef breed × Friesian calves are purchased from the summer/autumn flush of calvings in dairy herds the obvious targets are first calving at two years in autumn-calving herds and at 30 months in spring-calving herds.

Rearing management needs to recognise that modest levels of nutrition are consistent with the best lifetime production. In practice performance falls below these modest standards on all too many farms because of a lack of any systematic approach to heifer rearing.

The key production targets are weight and condition score at mating and calving (Table 11.14). Condition score targets are set at 3 for grazing heifers mating in the summer and autumn and slightly lower at $2\frac{1}{2}$ on winter rations for heifers for mating in winter and calving in the spring.

These target weights translate into performance targets which are modest, even for two year calving, provided sound management practices are

Table 11.14 Target weights and condition scores for dairy-bred calves reared as suckler herd replacements.

	Mating		Post calving	
	Liveweight (kg)	Condition score*	Liveweight (kg)	Condition score*
Spring calving at 2 years (summer mating)				
Angus/Hereford × F	375	3	475	2½
Limousin/Simmental × F	400	3	525	2½
Autumn calving at 2 years (winter mating)				
Angus/Hereford × F	350	2½	500	3
Limousin/Simmental × F	375	2½	550	3
Spring calving at 2½ years (summer mating)				
Angus/Hereford × F	450	3	525	2½
Limousin/Simmental × F	500	3	575	2½

F = Friesian
* On a scale 1 (thin) to 5 (fat)

adopted (Table 11.15). Good grazing gains are important and the leader/follower system is ideal with the younger heifers grazing ahead of the older generation. Rearing costs are minimised by holding gains at modest store levels during winter periods to capitalise on compensatory growth during the grazing season. If silage stocks are short winter rations can be based on straw.

The point has already been made that heifers should be mated to calve

Table 11.15 Targets for rearing autumn-born calves as suckler herd replacements calving at two years old.

	Angus/Hereford × Friesian	Limousin/Simmental × Friesian
Reared calf (kg)	95	105
Daily gain (kg)		
– rearing winter	0.6	0.6
– first summer	0.7	0.8
– second winter	0.6	0.6
– second summer	0.7	0.8
– overall	0.65	0.7
Concentrates (kg)	300	500
Silage (tonnes, 25% DM)	5.5	6.0
Stocking (cattle/ha)	1.7	1.6

early in the calving period to allow for delayed rebreeding which is almost inevitable after the first calving. It is wise to select an easy-calving breed such as Angus and Hereford, maybe an intermediate Limousin, for heifer matings unless an easy-calving AI bull is nominated.

Whatever sire breed is used calvings should be supervised closely and assistance given when necessary.

After calving on winter diets extra feed should be given to recognise that heifers are still growing as well as suckling a calf. This is essential if the target condition score at mating is to be achieved, particularly in the autumn calving herd.

THE ONCE BRED HEIFER

Beef production from heifers which are slaughtered soon after producing a calf, the once bred heifer, is an old idea. Its attraction is that, because the heifer produces a calf and then is slaughtered for beef herself, the system uses feed energy very efficiently compared to suckled calf production. However, because the system is difficult to manage it has never been adopted by farmers.

There are three factors which undermine the profitability of a once bred heifer system. First, there are problems in achieving high pregnancy rates in heifers mated to calve at 21–24 months of age. Second, calving difficulty and neonatal calf mortality can be very high at the first calving. And third, buyers are inclined to value bred heifers at the cow beef price which is 20 per cent below the maiden heifer price.

Because calving is aimed at less than two years of age performance targets have to be set higher than for replacement heifers. However, feeding needs to be eased off in the last six weeks before calving to avoid pushing up birthweights to a point where dystocia escalates.

Even with high standards of heifer rearing about 30 per cent of the heifers are likely to be barren. Pregnancy diagnosis is essential to identify these at an early stage so that they can be fed for slaughter as maiden heifers at 18 months of age.

Dystocia limits the range of sire breeds which can be used by natural service to easy calving breeds such as Angus and Hereford. However, if AI is used it is possible to choose continental breed sires which are proven for easy calving. In any event calving must be closely supervised.

Calves may be weaned a few days after calving and be fostered onto a cow, bucket-reared or sold. Alternatively a short suckling period of six weeks may be allowed at the end of which the calf is weaned on to solid feed.

Table 11.16 Tentative performance targets for beef production from once bred heifers using Limousin × Friesians.

Liveweight (kg)	
– mating (12 months)	350
– post-calving (21 – 24 months)	475
– sale – maiden heifers	475
– calved heifers	525
Heifers calving (%)	*70*

In both cases the dam is dried off by abrupt weaning which works surprisingly well, though dry cow therapy with antibiotic may be necessary to guard against mastitis.

After weaning a short finishing period of about six weeks is sufficient to restore any body condition lost in late pregnancy or during suckling.

At slaughter the killing-out percentage of once bred heifers is less than maiden heifers, partly because of the weight of udder. But carcases are heavier at the same fat class and of equally good carcase shape. What work has been done on eating quality suggests that the beef eats just as well as meat from maiden heifers, possibly with slightly better flavour. Nevertheless, buyers discriminate against bred heifers, assuming that bearing a calf makes the beef inferior. Such prejudice is hard to break down.

Tentative performance targets for once bred heifer production from Limousin × Friesians are presented in Table 11.16. This is not a beef system that can be recommended without drawing attention to its drawbacks.

The future possibility of being able to choose the sex of transferred embryos adds a new perspective to the discussion of producing beef from once bred heifers. It could be operated as an all female system. This would minimise calving difficulty because heifer calves are calved more easily than bulls and embryos could be bred specially for easy calving. Moreover, the whole system could be self-generating with heifers being reared, bred and then slaughtered for beef.

12 Finishing Suckled Calves and Stores

Yearling suckled calves which are well grown can be finished out of yards the following winter at 15–18 months of age. Large numbers of cattle of this type are traded at the autumn suckled calf sales. Lighter calves, most of them spring-born, are stored through the winter on a growing ration in preparation for grass finishing at 18–24 months. Frequently these are traded at the spring sales being purchased by specialist grass finishers. Those cattle which fail to finish off grass are finished the next winter at up to 30 months of age. It is now uncommon for cattle to pass through several store winters, as they used to, eventually finishing off grass at three or even four years old.

Suckler bull beef is a new development and spring-born calves can be finished during their first winter if they are fed a cereal/protein mix *ad libitum* until slaughter at a year of age or less. Alternatively a silage/cereal ration is fed over a longer finishing period with slaughter at 13–15 months.

Whichever finishing system is to be followed, cattle arriving at the finishing unit from the autumn sales are stressed. They may have been weaned and castrated only just before the sale and have experienced onerous journeys to and from the market as well as the sale itself. A common reaction is a form of pneumonia called 'transit fever' which seems to be more common nowadays. In its mildest form it may be no worse than a runny nose but at worst there is acute pneumonia. Cattle should be inspected frequently and treated with an antibiotic under veterinary supervision as soon as symptoms are spotted. It helps if the cattle are housed in airy buildings or, better still, can run out into an adjacent paddock.

Short-term finishing is very exposed to fluctuations in cattle prices, as a result of which finishers become highly preoccupied with buying and selling prices. The feeder's margin, the difference between sale and purchase price, is used all too often as a profit measure without realising that production efficiency still has major effects on profitability even when the finishing period is short.

It is self-evident that not every finisher can buy cheaper than the market average. There are buyers who know markets inside out and make a good living from their trading skills. They are few and far between. Everyone at a market needs to bid for cattle with a budget limit clearly in mind but also needs to realise that good management of cattle and grassland are essential to profitable production.

WINTER FINISHING

There is a wide range of slaughter ages and weights in winter finishing depending on the breed, age, weight and body condition of cattle at the start of the winter.

Steers fed silage/cereal diets are well suited to winter finishing be they British or continental breed crosses. Heifers are not as suitable because of their tendency to fatten too quickly. Nevertheless continental cross heifers are winter-finished profitably on high forage diets.

Specimen silage/cereal rations are shown in Table 12.1 for silage of 10 MJ ME per kg DM which should be the minimum target. The scope for manipulating rate of gain to alter the duration of the finishing period and fit in with silage supplies was discussed in Chapter 3 (see Table 3.9).

Other rations can be fed profitably including maize silage, roots, straw plus concentrates and various vegetable wastes. When plain or ammonia-treated straw is used as the bulk feed it is important to design rations which recognise that, because of its low nutrient value and intake, straw can make only a modest contribution to gains. On novel feeds particular care needs to be taken with ration design and not to be satisfied with modest performance just because the feeds appear to be cheap.

Targets for winter finishing suckled calves are shown in Table 12.2 (for suckler bull beef see Tables 12.4 and 12.5). The target stocking rates are based on a fertiliser application of 250 kg N per hectare. Grass silage beef

Table 12.1 Specimen silage/cereal rations for winter finishing suckled calves and stores.

Daily gain (kg):	0.8		1.0	
Liveweight (kg)	Silage (ME10, 25%DM)	Barley (ME12.8)	Silage	Barley
		kg fresh weight per day		
300	22	1	17	3
350	24	1	19	3
400	25	1½	20	3½
450	25	2	20	4½

Table 12.2 Targets for winter finishing suckled calves.

	Angus/Hereford crosses	Charolais/Limousin/ Simmental crosses	
	Steers	Steers	Heifers
Feeding period (months)	5	6	5
Start weight (kg)	320	350	310
Daily gain (kg)	0.9	1.0	0.8
Cereal (kg)	300	550	225
Silage (tonnes 25% DM)	3.2	3.4	3.5
Stocking (cattle/ha)	11	10	10
Slaughter weight (kg)	455	525	425
Carcase weight (kg)	250	295	235
Main carcase class (EUROP)	R/–U4L	–U/U+4L	–U4L

producers with a somewhat similar system manage grassland much more intensively. At their intensity stocking rates could be 50 per cent higher.

Results from commercial farms recorded by MLC (Table 12.3) show that producers with the top third of gross margins per head achieved above average gains on high silage rations. Having purchased suckled calves at slightly below the average price per kg, sale values were higher than average. So management and marketing were both important to top third success. It should be noted that these results were recorded in a year when margins were 50 per cent above the five year average.

Table 12.3 MLC Beefplan results from commercial farms winter finishing suckled calves. (Source: *MLC Beef Yearbook*, 1988.)

	Bottom third	Average gross margin per head	Top third
Gross margin per head (£)	49	98	148
Gross margin per ha (£)	408	947	1493
Feeding period (days)	170	173	188
Start weight (kg)	310	308	320
Daily gain (kg)	0.82	0.92	1.01
Cereal (kg)	560	574	429
Silage (tonnes)	2.5	2.5	3.8
Other feeds (tonnes)	0.5	0.3	0.3
Stocking (cattle/ha)	8.3	9.7	10.1
Slaughter weight (kg)	450	467	510

SUCKLER BULL BEEF

Suckler bull beef is a new development in Great Britain but is routine in continental European countries such as France, Italy and Spain. There is a huge trade in weaned suckled bull calves from France to the maize silage beeflots of northern Italy, amounting to some 700,000 cattle annually.

Bull beef production is easiest to organise in spring-calving herds because there is no need to separate bull and heifer calves before weaning in the autumn. It is possible in autumn-calving herds too, but only if the calving period is compact. Cows with bull calves need to be separated from those with heifers at six months of age.

Most bulls in continental Europe are finished on maize silage diets, though there is also grass finishing of heavyweight Charolais bulls in France. The tendency in France and Italy is to supplement the maize silage with high levels of maize grain so that silage DM accounts for only about 50 per cent of the total DM intake.

A higher dependence on maize silage is possible given its high nutritive value and intake. Tentative targets are presented in Table 12.4 for spring- and autumn-born Charolais cross bulls and similar breed types fed 1.5 kg of a 35 per cent crude protein supplement with maize silage to appetite. These targets would be applicable on farms able to grow maize in Great Britain.

In Britain suckler bull beef has developed along different lines from continental Europe. Beef specialists at Ministry Experimental Husbandry Farms have developed a rapid finishing system for spring-born bulls fed an all-concentrate diet from weaning. This is an attractive way of increasing the output from the suckler herd without requiring more land.

After weaning in the autumn the bulls are fed 1.5 kg per day of cereal/

Table 12.4 Targets for finishing suckler-bred bulls on maize silage.

	Charolais/Limousin/Simmental crosses	
	Autumn born	Spring born
Feeding period (months)	5	7
Start weight (kg)	350	250
Daily gain (kg)	1.2	1.2
Protein supplement (kg)	225	320
Maize silage (tonnes, 25% DM)	4.7	6.1
Slaughter weight (kg)	525	500
Carcase weight (kg)	295	280
Main carcase class (EUROP)	U3	U3

Table 12.5 Targets for suckler bull beef.

| | Charolais/Limousin/Simmental cross | | |
| | Spring born calf | | Autumn born calf |
	Cereal/protein	Silage/cereal	Silage/cereal
Feeding period (months)	6	8	5
Start weight (kg)	245	245	350
Daily gain (kg)	1.4	1.1	1.1
Cereal/protein (tonnes)	1.3	—	—
Cereal (tonnes)	—	0.7	0.5
Silage (tonnes, 25% DM)	—	4.8	3.2
Slaughter weight (kg)	500	520	525
Carcase weight (kg)	280	290	295
Main carcase class (EUROP)	U3	U3	U3

protein (14 per cent crude protein) with straw to appetite. Then the cereal/ protein allowance is increased gradually to *ad libitum* fed from a hopper providing 100 mm trough space per bull. The gradual changeover is essential to avoid the risk of acidosis.

Spectacular growth rates have been achieved in the trials with slaughter weights of 500 kg achieved at less than a year of age but the targets in Table 12.5 are more cautious and allow for modest gains in the changeover period. The table also presents targets for finishing suckler bulls on good quality silage supplemented with cereal. As yet there are two few recorded results from farms to validate the targets.

All of the provisos about safe handling of bulls referred to in Chapters 6 and 10 apply equally to suckler bull beef.

OVERWINTERING STORES

Grass finishers buying store cattle in the spring have always preferred cattle with hairy coats which have been fed moderately through the winter, knowing that they will grow fastest at grass. This phenomenon, called compensatory growth, should be exploited whenever cattle are being fed through the winter in preparation for grazing.

Daily gains during the winter and during grazing are inversely related which implies that the lower the winter gain the better. But time comes into the equation too and with grass finishing it is important that slaughter

Table 12.6 Specimen rations for overwintering.

Daily gain (kg): Liveweight	0.6	0.6			0.8	
	Silage*	Straw**	Concentrates		Silage	Cereal
250	21	3.5	2.5		18	1
300	23	3.5	3		22	1
350	27	3.75	3.5		24	1
400	28	4.25	3.5		25	1.5

* Silage 10 MJ ME per kg DM, 25%DM
** Plain barley straw

begins soon after mid-season so that cattle numbers can be reduced in step with declining grass production. This interacts with breed type and sex because late maturing cattle take longer to reach market condition.

On balance the best advice is to overwinter steers of British breed crosses and continental cross heifers at a gain of 0.6 kg per day and continental cross steers at 0.8 per day. Specimen rations are presented in Table 12.6 which demonstrates that straw can contribute usefully to the ration at the lower rate of gain; arable by-products are also useful.

If cattle are being overwintered for sale as stores in the spring the producer has to balance the higher value per kg paid for stores in plain condition against the lower weight sold if gains are held down. The outcome is likely to be gains at least at the levels recommended earlier, slightly higher if the gains can be made from high quality silage with a low level of cereal supplementation.

GRASS FINISHING

Grassland management for finishing store cattle is simpler than managing a dairy beef system because the grazing batch of cattle is usually alone on the farm with no younger age group to worry about. Also, on specialist grass finishing farms which buy their cattle in the spring there is no conservation requirement. Incidentally it could be argued that this is a disadvantage because there are no fresh aftermaths to graze later in the season.

In this chapter overwintering and grass finishing are considered as two parts of a single annual system.

Steers, heifers and the whole range of breed types are all suitable for grass finishing. The targets in Table 12.7 are for continental breed crosses on

Table 12.7 Targets for grass finishing suckler-bred store cattle.

| | Charolais/Limousin/Simmental crosses | |
	Steers	Heifers
Overwintering		
Feeding period (months)	6	6
Start weight (kg)	250	230
Daily gain (kg)	0.8	0.6
Cereal (kg)	200	—
Silage (tonnes, 25% DM)	4.0	4.0
Turnout weight (kg)	400	350
Grass finishing		
Feeding period (months)	5	4
Daily gain (kg)	1.0	0.9
Cereal (kg)	75	35
Overall stocking rate (cattle/ha)	4.0	4.3
Slaughter weight (kg)	550	460
Carcase weight (kg)	310	255
Main carcase class (EUROP)	U4L	U4L

grassland fertilised with 250 kg N per hectare. They incorporate the thinking on relationships between earliness of maturity and grass finishing performance outlined in Chapter 4.

At turnout it is worth feeding 1–2 kg concentrates per day for the first two or three weeks. Between 60 and 65 per cent of the grassland is needed for grazing in the early part of the season with about 25 per cent split off as a grazing buffer. Grazing management should aim to maintain sward height at 6–8 cm until mid-season, grazing part or all of the buffer if necessary to achieve this, and allow the sward to increase to 8–10 cm later in the season. The conservation area (and as much of the buffer area as possible) should be cut early for silage with a second cut from part of the area later in the season. Aftermaths should be grazed as required and it may be necessary to reintroduce supplementary concentrate feeding in August.

If suckled calves were dosed for worms at yarding no further anthelmintic control should be necessary.

MLC Beefplan results from recorded overwintering and grass finishing units (Table 12.8) show that, whilst overwintering gains were of the right order, grazing gains were not up to standard, even on units with the top third of gross margins per hectare. There is considerable scope for improvement through control of sward height, setting up a grazing buffer, intelligent use

Table 12.8 MLC Beefplan results from recorded overwintering and grass finishing units 1987.
(Source: *MLC Beef Yearbook*, 1988)

	Bottom third	Average gross margin per hectare	Top third
Gross margin per head (£)	89	108	126
Gross margin per ha (£)	271	439	640
Overwinter (days)	190	182	202
Grazing (days)	138	131	116
Start weight (kg)	252	260	275
Overwinter gain (kg/day)	0.50	0.55	0.60
Turnout weight (kg)	347	360	396
Cereal (kg)	435	332	395
Silage (tonnes)	3.5	3.5	4.0
Overall stocking rate (cattle/ha)	3.0	4.1	5.1
Grazing gain (kg/day)	0.78	0.81	0.83
Slaughter weight (kg)	455	466	492

of aftermath grazing from mid-season and strategic use of supplementary concentrates at either end of the grazing season.

Many grass finishers use such low levels of N fertiliser that a switch to clover swards could be made with little or no fall in stocking rate. Allied to reduced fertiliser costs there could be an increase both in gross margin per head and per hectare. However, the point has already been made that clover swards are not the easy option. On the contrary they are more difficult to establish and manage than grass swards. The switch would be precipitated by a decision to produce beef under an 'organic' label.

MARKETING SUCKLER BEEF

Suckler beef is top of the meat trade range and justifiably commands premium prices. Carcases are of good shape, meat yields are consistently higher than dairy beef and the meat seems to have the edge on eating quality.

Many deadweight buyers fail to pay extra premiums for the best conformation carcases, lumping –U, U+ and E into a single price band. This situation is changing under the pressure of what are considered to be greater premiums in live auction markets, though as yet there are no auction price reports of quality differentials to confirm this one way or the other.

The main danger with this category of cattle is allowing them to slip into fat class 4H. Heifers are a particular problem because of their earlier maturity than steers. Even in the traditional quality trade there are fewer and fewer buyers looking for carcases as fat as this and most of them penalise 4H carcases quite severely.

In winter finishing there is a premium trade at Christmas after which prices fall back until the seasonal price rise becomes established in the spring. Marketing strategy becomes influenced increasingly as the winter progresses by the status of feed stocks. Within this limitation there is still a case for marketing slow-growing cattle as soon as they are fit to sell and allowing fast growers to progress profitably to the upper end of the buyer's preferred weight range.

Grass-finished cattle are sold into a falling market. Prices dip in June, or as soon as hot weather arrives, and fall by up to 2p per kg liveweight per month to a seasonal low in October. This is an argument for early marketing. On the other hand, grass puts on gains cheaply which increases value. So what should be the marketing policy?

The higher the daily gain the stronger is the case for retaining cattle against the seasonal price trend provided they stay in the preferred weight range and do not become overfat. At present prices a steer gaining 1.0 kg per day could easily gain £120 in value between June and October despite a seasonal price fall of 1p per kg liveweight per month, whereas one gaining 0.6 kg would increase in value by only half as much.

Suckler bull beef carcases combine excellent conformation with leanness. The market has hardly had time to get used to this new product but already pays higher prices than for equivalent steers. However, premiums vary and so it is important to explore local outlets to find the best price.

Index